GRAMMAR
Form and Function

3A

Workbook

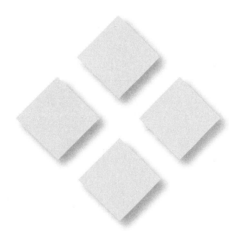

Milada Broukal
Diana Renn
Amy Parker

Grammar Form and Function 3A Workbook

 This book is printed on recycled, acid-free paper containing 10% postconsumer waste.

1 2 3 4 5 6 7 8 9 QPD 9 8 7 6 5 4 3 2 1

ISBN: 0-07-310411-6

Editorial director: Tina B. Carver
Executive editor: Erik Gundersen
Senior developmental editor: Annie Sullivan
Editorial assistant: Kasey Williamson
Production manager: MaryRose Malley
Cover design: Preface, Inc.
Interior design: Preface, Inc.

Photo credits:
All photos are courtesy of Getty Images Royalty-Free Collection.

Contents

UNIT 1 THE PRESENT TENSES

1a The Simple Present Tense and The Present Progressive Tense

Student Book p. 2

1 Practice

Complete the sentences with the simple present or the present progressive of the verbs in parentheses. If there are other words in the parentheses, include them.

Jenna: Hi, Mark! I (never, see)

_____ you outside
    ₁

this early in the morning. Where

(you, go) _____?
        ₂

Mark: I (run) _____ to
        ₃

the park right now. These days I

(try) _____ to work
    ₄

out every morning before work. I (want) _____ to lose
                                ₅

weight. My doctor said that exercise (be) _____ the most
                                    ₆

important thing you can do. What about you? Why (be) _____
                                            ₇

you up so early?

Jenna: I (work out) _____ this morning, too. I usually
            ₈

(get up) _____ at six to work out.
        ₉

Mark: That's great. What (you, do) _____ to stay in shape?
                            ₁₀

Jenna: Sometimes I (jog) _____ around the neighborhood. I often
                ₁₁

(take) _____ a yoga class at the gym. But unfortunately, it
    ₁₂

(become) _____ more difficult to find the time and energy
        ₁₃

to exercise.

Mark: Oh, really? Why (be) _____ it so hard?
                    ₁₄

(be) _____ you busy with work?
    ₁₅

Jenna: Yes, I (be) _____₁₆. Sometimes I

(come) _____₁₇ home late, and often I

(stay) _____₁₈ up late finishing work. It

(get) _____₁₉ harder to wake up early.

Mark: It (be) _____₂₀ hard for me to get up in the morning and

exercise, too. But I (not, be) _____₂₁ busy with work. I just

(not, like) _____₂₂ to exercise!

2 Practice

Complete the questions and answers with the simple present or the present progressive of the verbs in parentheses. If there are other words in the parentheses, include them.

Doctor: How (you, feel) _____₁

these days, Rob?

Rob: I (not, do) _____₂

very well at the moment. I hurt my knee

last Sunday, and the pain (get)

_____₃ worse. My knee

(constantly, hurt) _____₄.

Doctor: (you, take) _____₅

any medication right now?

Rob: No, I (not, take) _____₆ anything at the moment.

Doctor: (you, exercise) _____₇ regularly?

Rob: No, I don't. I (not, have, usually) _____₈ time. Although

I (play, sometimes) _____₉ basketball with my friends on

weekends.

Doctor: Which knee (bother) _____₁₀ you?

Rob: My right knee.

Doctor: (it, hurt) _____₁₁ when you bend your knee?

Rob: No, it (not, do) _____. But I (feel, always)
                            12
_____ pain when I straighten it.
           13

Doctor: How (your knee, feel) _____ when I move it this way?
                                    14

Rob: Ouch!

Doctor: You needed to see a doctor as soon as this happened. Who

(be) _____ your regular doctor?
              15

Rob: I (see, usually) _____ Dr. Berman. But he
                            16

(be) _____ on vacation this week.
              17

3   Practice

Match the sentences with the uses of the simple present and the present progressive.

Simple Present Tense	Present Progressive Tense
a. permanent situation	d. action in progress
b. repeated action	e. changing situation
c. general truth	f. action in progress around the present

_____ 1. Susan works as a programmer at a computer company in Seattle.

_____ 2. Many people in the computer industry are losing their jobs these days.

_____ 3. There used to be many programming jobs in Seattle, but it is getting more difficult to find a job in today's economy.

_____ 4. Many companies advertise jobs in the newspaper.

_____ 5. Susan reads the job ads every morning.

_____ 6. A company called "Software Solutions" is hiring computer programmers right now!

4 Practice

Read the sentences. Write _C_ next to the sentence if the simple present or the present progressive is used correctly. Write _I_ if it is used incorrectly.

_____ **1.** Why you studying English at this school?

_____ **2.** Public transportation becomes more important in our crowded city.

_____ **3.** My sister is constantly borrowing my clothes.

_____ **4.** Because of her new diet, she's not eat bread now.

_____ **5.** These days, I'm working part time and going to school.

_____ **6.** Which movie you want to see?

_____ **7.** In the evenings, we like to walk around the neighborhood.

_____ **8.** Where do you working at present?

5 Practice

Look at the photo. Write four sentences using the simple present and four sentences using the present progressive. Try to include some negatives and questions.

Simple Present

1. _____

_____

2. _____

_____

3. _____

_____

4. _____

Present Progressive

5. _____

6. _____

7. _____

8. _____

6 | Practice

Complete the sentences with the simple present or the present progressive of the verbs in parentheses. If there are negative words in the parentheses, include them.

---

27   **January 10, 2005**

Restaurant Review: The Boston Bistro

If you (look) _____ for
                           1

excellent food and a pleasant dining experience, do not

eat at the Boston Bistro. First of all, the food

(be) _____ terrible. The meat
            2

(be) _____ tough and overcooked; it
            3

(require) _____ a very sharp knife to cut it.
         4

I (love) _____ garlic, but the pasta sauce
        5

(smell) _____ too strongly of garlic. Strangely,
      6

the sauce (not, taste) _____ like garlic — it (seem) _____
                  7   **8**

to have no flavor at all! Finally, the menu (not, have) _____ many choices.
                                              9

The food (not, be) _____ the only bad part of the Boston Bistro. The
                    10

dining room (appear) _____ crowded because there are so many tables
                11

pushed together. Personally, I usually (not, enjoy) _____ the sound of loud
                                    12

conversations around me while I (try) _____ to enjoy a quiet meal. Also,
                         13

the servers always (seem) _____ too busy to pay attention to you.
                14

Above all, the food (cost) _____ too much. I (realize)
                        15

_____ many nice restaurants (charge) _____ more than
      16   **17**

$25.00 for dinner these days. But for $28.00, I (prefer) _____ to have
                                  18

excellent food and excellent service. I (fear) _____ that at those high
                         19

prices, the Boston Bistro won't be in business for long.

---

7 Practice

Decide if each sentence has a stative or an active meaning. Then complete the sentences with the correct form of the verbs in parentheses.

1. (think)

He _____ about quitting his job. However, he _____ _____ it might be a bad idea.

2. (taste)

She _____ the ice cream cone right now. It _____ like a coconut.

3. (smell)

The refrigerator

_____

terrible. She _____

_____

the refrigerator after returning from her vacation.

4. (appear)

The woman _____ very tired. She _____ in a play every night this week.

5. (be)

She _____ very quiet. She _____ quiet because she is working in a library.

The Present Perfect Tense and The Present Perfect Progressive Tense

Student Book p. 11

8 │ Practice

Complete the sentences with the present perfect or the present perfect progressive of the verbs in parentheses. Sometimes both tenses are possible. If both are possible, use the present perfect progressive.

A. Rachel, Eric, and Denise (graduate, just)

_____! They (attend)
                1

_____ this school for
                2

the past four years. All three of them

(wait) _____ a long time for this
                3

special day. Rachel (study) _____
                                        4

music, and she plans to continue her musical

studies in the future. Eric (find, already) _____ a good job in
                                                        5

a bank. Denise (decide) _____ to travel — she
                                    6

(not, go) _____ anywhere since she started school. They
                7

(not, say) _____ goodbye to all of their friends yet, and they
                8

(still, not, remove) _____ their graduation caps and gowns.
                                9

They (be) _____ too busy celebrating their success.
                        10

B. Adina (try) _____ to
1
improve her grades in math for months. So far, her

grades (improve) _____.
2
Her teacher, Mr. Williams, (help)

_____ her. She
3
(study) _____ math for
4
two hours every night. She

(review) _____ all the
5
chapters in her math book. Adina (never, be)

_____ very good at math. She
6
(not, earn) _____ an "A" in math since she was in the ninth grade.
7
She (always, prefer) _____ English and foreign languages. But she
8
(just, receive) _____ an "A" on her math test.
9

9 Practice

Circle the adverbs and time expressions. Then complete the sentences with the simple past, present perfect, or present perfect progressive of the verbs in parentheses. If either the present perfect or present perfect progressive is possible, use the present perfect progressive.

A. Robin: _____ (you, borrow) my new dress last night?
1

Joanna: No, I (not, do) _____. I (not, borrow)
2

_____ your clothes in a long time. Ever since I
3

gained a few pounds, I (not, be able to) _____
4

fit into your clothes.

Robin: That's strange. I (think) _____ I put the dress in my
5

closet right after I (come) _____ home yesterday.
6

B. Erica: I like your new car! When (you, buy) _____ it?

1

David: I (buy) _____ it at 2:00 today. I (only, have)

2

_____ it for a few hours!

3

Erica: It's really bright. I (never, see) _____ you in such a

4

colorful car. (you, own, ever) _____ a red car

5

before?

David: No, this is my first. I (always, prefer) _____ black

6

cars. I (drive) _____ a black car since the day I

7

(get) _____ my driver's license.

8

Erica: So why (you, decide) _____ to buy a red car?

9

David: This one (be) _____ on sale!

10

C. Samantha: (you, watch) _____ the baseball game last night?

1

Ron: No, I (do, not) _____. I (never, like)

2

_____ baseball.

3

Samantha: You're kidding! Baseball (be) _____ this country's

4

most popular sport for almost 100 years! Everybody likes baseball!

Ron: Not me. I prefer soccer. I (be) _____ a soccer fan

5

since I was a kid. And I (play) _____ the game for

6

about ten years. (you, ever, see) _____ the World

7

Cup on TV? Now that's exciting to watch.

Samantha: I (watch) _____ the World Cup two years ago. You're

8

right; it (be) _____ exciting to watch. I think

9

Americans (grow) _____ more interested in soccer in

10

recent years. But I still like baseball better.

10 Practice

Circle the correct adverb and put it in the correct position. Only one adverb is correct. Rewrite each sentence with the adverb in the correct place.

1. Gina has walked to work in her new shoes. (still / just / ever)

   _____

   _____

2. She has worn such uncomfortable shoes. (ever / yet / never)

   _____

   _____

3. It is only 9:00 in the morning, but her feet have started to hurt. (yet / still / already)

   _____

   _____

4. She hasn't arrived at work. (already / yet / just)

   _____

11 Practice

Rewrite each sentence in Practice 10 as a question. Use the present perfect or present perfect progressive. Change adverbs if necessary.

1. _____ ?

2. _____ ?

3. _____ ?

4. _____ ?

12 Practice

Read the sentences. Write *C* next to the sentence if the present perfect or the present perfect progressive is used correctly. Write *I* if it is used incorrectly.

_____ 1. She's been having that coat for a week.

_____ 2. I so far have traveled to five countries and thirty states.

_____ 3. The students have been waiting for the teacher since 20 minutes.

_____ 4. Have they already paid for their tickets?

_____ 5. Where has the time gone?

_____ 6. Have ever you been to Africa?

_____ 7. He hasn't returned the homework already.

_____ 8. Women have been earned more money for the last ten years.

_____ 9. How many times have you been taking the TOEFL?

_____ 10. We've never been to that restaurant.

13 Practice

Write five statements and two questions about the people in the photo. Use the tenses given in parentheses and time expressions, adverbs, or negatives when possible.

1. (present perfect)

_____

2. (present perfect progressive)

_____

3. (simple past)

_____

4. (simple present)

_____

5. (present progressive)

_____

6. (Question: present perfect)

_____

7. (Question: present perfect progressive)

_____

SELF-TEST

A **Choose the best answer, A, B, C, or D, to complete the sentence. Mark your answer by darkening the oval with the same letter.**

1. Who _____ to join us for lunch?

   A. does want   Ⓐ Ⓑ Ⓒ Ⓓ
   B. is wanting
   C. wants
   D. wanting

2. Many students _____ at part-time jobs these days.

   A. have worked   Ⓐ Ⓑ Ⓒ Ⓓ
   B. are working
   C. working
   D. are being working

3. Basketball players _____ usually tall.

   A. are being   Ⓐ Ⓑ Ⓒ Ⓓ
   B. are
   C. have been
   D. being

4. What grade _____ in that class?

   A. are you having   Ⓐ Ⓑ Ⓒ Ⓓ
   B. you have
   C. have
   D. do you have

5. Fresh coffee _____ good in the morning.

   A. is smelling   Ⓐ Ⓑ Ⓒ Ⓓ
   B. has been smelling
   C. smells
   D. smelling

6. Anne: Are you enjoying that book?
   Ron: Yes, _____.

   A. I'm   Ⓐ Ⓑ Ⓒ Ⓓ
   B. I have
   C. I am
   D. I do

7. Right now, she _____ about her vacation.

   A. thinks   Ⓐ Ⓑ Ⓒ Ⓓ
   B. has thought
   C. has been thinking
   D. is thinking

8. The class _____ $100 for their trip.

   A. earns   Ⓐ Ⓑ Ⓒ Ⓓ
   B. has earned
   C. has been earning
   D. earning

9. She _____ to borrow her parents' car.

   A. is constantly asking   Ⓐ Ⓑ Ⓒ Ⓓ
   B. constantly asking
   C. asking constantly
   D. is constantly asks

10. Why _____ TV for four hours?

   A. they have watched   Ⓐ Ⓑ Ⓒ Ⓓ
   B. have they watched
   C. have they been watching
   D. they are watching

B Find the underlined word or phrase, A, B, C, or D, that is incorrect. Mark your answer by darkening the oval with the same letter.

1. He <u>hasn't</u> <u>answered</u> <u>so far</u> our question
   A   B   C
   <u>about the</u> test.
   D

   Ⓐ Ⓑ Ⓒ Ⓓ

2. Mary <u>hasn't</u> <u>been</u> <u>work</u> <u>at her new job</u> for
        A   B   C   D
   very long.

   Ⓐ Ⓑ Ⓒ Ⓓ

3. <u>Where</u> <u>the baseball team has</u> <u>been</u>
    A   B   C
   <u>practicing</u> during the winter?
    D

   Ⓐ Ⓑ Ⓒ Ⓓ

4. <u>Have you</u> <u>yet</u> <u>signed up</u> for <u>the class?</u>
    A   B   C   D

   Ⓐ Ⓑ Ⓒ Ⓓ

5. <u>Her</u> mother <u>has been</u> <u>waiting</u> for her
    A   B   C
   <u>for 3:00</u> in the afternoon.
    D

   Ⓐ Ⓑ Ⓒ Ⓓ

6. The workers <u>are</u> <u>painting</u> the fence <u>since</u>
                A   B   C
   early <u>this morning</u>.
          D

   Ⓐ Ⓑ Ⓒ Ⓓ

7. I <u>haven't</u> <u>been</u> <u>still</u> to <u>any countries</u> in
       A   B   C   D
   Asia.

   Ⓐ Ⓑ Ⓒ Ⓓ

8. What is the most <u>exciting</u> thing you <u>have</u>
                     A   B
   <u>ever</u> <u>do?</u>
    C   D

   Ⓐ Ⓑ Ⓒ Ⓓ

9. <u>Is</u> the president <u>appears</u> on <u>any TV shows</u>
    A   B   C
   <u>this week?</u>
    D

   Ⓐ Ⓑ Ⓒ Ⓓ

10. <u>Some</u> older people <u>are believing</u> that
     A   B
    teenagers <u>are becoming</u> more <u>polite</u>
                C   D
    these days.

    Ⓐ Ⓑ Ⓒ Ⓓ

UNIT 2 THE PAST TENSES

2a The Simple Past Tense and The Past Progressive Tense
Student Book p. 28

1 | Practice

Complete the sentences with the simple past or the past progressive of the verbs in parentheses. If there are other words in the parentheses, include them.

Police Beat: A List of Last Week's Neighborhood Crimes

A. On Saturday, April 12, a 70-year-old woman (report) _____ that her purse
                                                                1
was stolen at Bradshaw's Supermarket. She (wait) _____ in the checkout line
                                                           2
when she suddenly (realize) _____ she needed to buy milk. When she (leave)
                                     3
_____ her grocery cart to get the milk, she (forget) _____ to
        4   5
take her purse with her. When she (return) _____ to the cart, her purse
                                                    6
(be) _____ gone. There (be) _____ two other people in line,
         7   8
two men in their 30s. The woman (ask) _____ them about her purse. They
                                               9
(not, see) _____ anything happen while they (stand) _____ in line.
                  10   11
They (say) _____ that maybe she had left her purse somewhere else.
                 12

B. At 7:00 P.M. on Thursday, April 10, a man on Maple Street (water) _____
                                                                                  1
his yard when he (hear) _____ a woman screaming. He immediately
                                2
(call) _____ the police on his cell phone. Then he (drop) _____ the
           3   4
hose and (run) _____ in the direction of the screams. At the end of the block,
                       5
he (see) _____ a tall man in a blue jacket trying to take the woman's briefcase.
                 6
When the tall man (notice) _____ the neighbor, he (stop) _____
                                    7   8
what he (do) _____, (let) _____ go of the briefcase, and (turn)
                     9   10
_____ to leave. At first he (not, seem) _____ worried about the
        11   12
neighbor, but then he suddenly (start) _____ to run. The neighbor
                                                13
(not, want) _____ the man to escape before the police (come)
                   14
_____. He (yell) _____ at the tall man to stop. While the man
        15   16

(escape) _____, he (trip) _____ over his shoelace and (fall)
       17   **18**
_____ to the ground. Seconds later, while he (try) _____ to stand
       19   **20**
up, police (arrive) _____ on the scene and (arrest) _____ the man.
                          21   **22**

2 Practice

Complete the sentences with the simple past or the past progressive of the verbs in parentheses. If there are other words in the parentheses, include them.

Mike Willis's life has always included bicycles.

Even as a very small child, he (love) _____
                                              1

bicycles. His parents (give) _____ him a
                                    2

bike when he (be) _____ only four years
                        3

old. In high school, he (compete) _____
                                         4

in many races, and he (win) _____ a lot
                                   5

of money.

One day, while he (train) _____ for
                                6

a big race, he (feel) _____ a sharp pain in his chest. He (ignore)
                            7

_____ it and kept riding. But as days (pass) _____, the pain
       8   **9**

(not, go) _____ away. And it (get) _____ harder for him to ride
                 10   **11**

his bike up hills or long distances.

Mike's parents (be) _____ very worried about their son. They (think)
                           12

_____ he had a virus. They (take) _____ him to the doctor. The
       13   **14**

doctor (do) _____ many tests on Mike's blood.
                   15

The next day, while Mike (fix) _____ the gears on his bicycle, the doctor
                                      16

(call) _____. He (ask) _____ Mike to come to his office. There,
             17   **18**

the doctor (say) _____ that he (have) _____ a rare and very
                        19   **20**

dangerous form of cancer. That same day, Mike (decide) _____ to do all he
                                                                  21

could to fight this disease. And he (promise) _____ himself that if he (get)
                                                     22

_____ well, he would help other people with cancer.
       23

Mike (keep) _____ his promise. Six months after he (recover)
                    24
_____ from cancer, he (begin) _____ riding his bike. Eight
        25   26
months later, he (go) _____ on long rides again. In 2001, he (start)
                              27
_____ an annual bike riding event to raise money for cancer research. Three
        28
years later, more than 500 cyclists (participate) _____ in this event. In
                                                          29
2004, the event (raise) _____ nearly one million dollars for cancer research.
                                30

3 | Practice

Use the prompts to write yes/no questions and answers about Mike Willis. Use the simple past or the past progressive.

1. Mike / love / bicycles / as a child

Question: _____?

Answer: _____.

2. he / win / a lot of money / from bicycle races

Question: _____?

Answer: _____.

3. Mike / see / a doctor / as soon as he felt pain

Question: _____?

Answer: _____.

4. Mike's parents / worried / about him

Question: _____?

Answer: _____.

5. Mike / ride / his bike / while he was sick

Question: _____?

Answer: _____.

6. Mike / ride / his bike / by 2001

Question: _____?

Answer: _____.

4 Practice

Use the question words to write questions about Mike Willis for the answers that follow.

1. Question: When _____?

   Answer: Mike's parents gave him a bicycle when he was four years old.

2. Question: When _____?

   Answer: He first felt a pain in his chest while he was training for a big race.

3. Question: What _____?

   Answer: They thought he had a virus.

4. Question: What _____?

   Answer: Mike was fixing the gears on his bike when the doctor called.

5. Question: How soon after his recovery _____?

   Answer: Mike was going on long bike rides eight months after his recovery.

6. Question: How much _____?

   Answer: Mike's event raised nearly one million dollars in 2004.

7. Question: Why _____?

   Answer: Mike started this event because he promised to help people fight cancer.

5 Practice

Read the sentences. What does each sentence mean? Circle *a* or *b*.

1. My sister was very happy when she learned she got the job.

   a. First she was happy, and then she learned she got the job.

   b. She learned she got the job, and then she was very happy.

2. My sister was wondering if she should go back to school when she learned she got the job.

   a. First she was wondering if she should go back to school, and then she learned she got the job.

   b. She learned she got the job, and then she wondered if she should go back to school.

3. Our parents cried when they heard the good news.

   a. First our parents heard the good news, and then they cried.

   b. Our parents were crying, and then they heard the good news.

4. While Jack was traveling in Europe, his dog died.

    a. First Jack's dog died, and then Jack traveled in Europe.

    b. Jack went to Europe, and then his dog died.

5. Rosa called her sister when she heard that the baby was born.

    a. First Rosa heard that the baby was born, and then she called her sister.

    b. Rosa called her sister, and then the baby was born.

6. Tom's girlfriend came over while he was taking a nap.

    a. First Tom started to take a nap, and then his girlfriend came over.

    b. Tom's girlfriend came over, and then Tom took a nap.

6 Practice

Combine the sentences into one using *while* or *when*. Use correct punctuation.

1. I studied for the final exam. I didn't want to hear the TV or the phone.

While _____.

2. I worked at two jobs. I never had any free time.

_____ while _____.

3. My friends were upset. They heard we were moving to another city.

When _____.

4. Elizabeth turned 16. More than 100 guests came to her birthday party.

_____ when _____.

5. Josh applied to colleges. His parents hoped he would stay close to home.

While _____.

7 Practice

Rewrite the sentences in Practice 6 with the *when* and *while* clauses in reverse order. Use correct punctuation.

1. _____.

2. _____.

3. _____.

4. _____.

5. _____.

8 Practice

Complete the sentences with information about you, your friends, or your family.

1. _____ felt really embarrassed when _____

_____.

2. _____ was very afraid when _____

_____.

3. When _____,

_____ was very sad.

4. When _____,

_____ was extremely happy.

9 Practice

Choose one of the sentences you wrote in Practice 8. Use it as the first sentence of a paragraph. In at least six sentences, give more information about what happened. Use the simple past and the past progressive tenses as you tell the story.

_____

_____

_____

_____

_____

_____

_____

_____

_____

_____

_____

2b The Past Perfect Tense and The Past Perfect Progressive Tense

Student Book p. 36

10 Practice

Complete the sentences with the simple past or the past perfect of the verbs in parentheses. If there are other words in the parentheses, include them.

Have you ever won any money? My friend

Jason (feel) _____ like he did
              1

yesterday. After work, he

(go) _____ to the bank to get
        2

some money. He (want) _____
                           3

to take his girlfriend Lisa out to dinner at a

nice restaurant. They (not, eat)

_____ at a nice restaurant for weeks. Since he (just, be) _____
       4   5

paid at work, he (think) _____ it would be fun to spend a little more
                              6

money.

At the cash machine, he (ask) _____ for $100.00. He
                                       7

(be) _____ very surprised when a large number of $20.00 bills
        8

(start) _____ flying out! He (never, see) _____
          9   10

so much cash at one time. He (be) _____ alone at the machine,
                                        11

and he (not, know) _____ what to do. He (wonder) _____
                         12   13

if this (happen, ever) _____ to anyone else.
                            14

Finally, the money (stop) _____ coming out. Jason
                               15

(take) _____ the $20 bills from the ground and
          16

(count) _____ them. He (could not, believe) _____
           17   18

his luck. Just a few minutes earlier, he (think) _____ about taking his
                                                      19

girlfriend somewhere nice. Now he could take her to the nicest place in town!

He (put) _____ the money in his wallet. He
20

(walk) _____ away from the machine. Then he
21

(wonder) _____ if he (do) _____ the right thing.
22   23

Maybe the machine (be) _____ broken. If so, the money
24

(not, be) _____ his to keep. Jason (bring) _____
25   26

the money into the bank and (tell) _____ the manager what
27

(happen) _____ to him at the cash machine. The manager said
28

she (never, hear) _____ of that happening before. She
29

(be) _____ very glad that Jason (return) _____
30   31

the money.

Jason (take) _____ Lisa out to dinner later that night, for less
32

than $100. Lisa (be) _____ happy. She (say) _____
33   34

it was the nicest evening she (enjoy) _____ in a long time. Then she
35

said that Jason (spend) _____ too much money.
36

II Practice

Someone took this photo of Alyssa yesterday. Why did she look so happy? Complete the sentences using the prompts and the past perfect or the past perfect progressive.

1. (get a new job)

   She looked happy because

   _____.

2. (buy some new clothes)

   She looked happy because

   _____.

3. (work out during her lunch hour)

   She looked happy because _____.

4. (not / listen to the bad news on TV)

She looked happy because _____.

5. *(your idea)*

She looked happy because _____.

6. *(your idea)*

She looked happy because _____.

12 Practice

A journalist is interviewing an actor about his new movie. Use the prompts to write questions for the actor's answers. Write the questions in the simple past, the past perfect, or the past perfect progressive.

1. Question: When _____?

Answer: I made this movie last summer.

2. Question: _____?

Answer: No, I had never been in an action movie before.

3. Question: What kinds of movies _____?

Answer: I had acted in romances and comedies.

4. Question: Why _____?

Answer: I'd never done action movies because I wasn't in very good shape.

5. Question: Where _____?

Answer: They filmed this movie in Turkey and in France.

6. Question: _____?

Answer: No, I hadn't visited either of those countries before.

7. Question: What _____?

Answer: Before I made this movie, I'd been taking a break from acting.

8. Question: Where _____?

Answer: I'd been living in Los Angeles before I moved to New York.

9. Question: How long _____?

   Answer: I'd been working in L.A. for about five years.

10. Question: How many _____?

    Answer: I'd starred in eight movies.

13 Practice

Write six sentences about what you had or hadn't done (or been doing) by the time you sat down to do this exercise. Write three sentences using the past perfect and three sentences using the past perfect progressive. Use some negatives.

1. _____.

2. _____.

3. _____.

4. _____.

5. _____.

6. _____.

14 Practice

Complete the sentences with the present perfect progressive or the past perfect progressive of the verbs in parentheses.

1. The Larsen family is moving today. They (pack) _____ boxes since 6:00 in the morning.

2. Yesterday, they (pack) _____ for ten hours before they finally went to bed.

3. They're excited because they (want) _____ a bigger home for years.

4. Before they found this new home, they (complain) _____ that their apartment was too small for three people and two dogs.

5. They (move) _____ the furniture around, but it hadn't worked.

6. The Larsens were happy to find this new house because they (look) _____ for a long time.

15 Practice

Underline the correct forms in parentheses.

A.

1. When my grandparents were young, many people (had smoked / used to smoke) in public places.

2. Where (did people use to / people would) smoke?

3. People (would smoke / use to smoke) in almost any public place, including restaurants and movie theaters.

4. They (wouldn't think / didn't use to think) that smoking was dangerous.

5. My grandfather (would start / started) smoking back in college.

6. At that time, students and professors (had / would have) very different attitudes about cigarettes.

7. Some students (used to light / were used to light) cigarettes in the classroom!

B.

1. Romance today is different from in the past. In the 1940s, a man (used to "court" / was used to "court") a woman.

2. A true gentleman (would used to bring / would bring) a woman flowers every time he came to see her.

3. A woman (would try / used to trying) to win his love with clever conversation and charm, not just with appearance.

4. My grandmother (won / used to win) my grandfather's heart this way in 1941.

5. In that same year, he (used to ask / asked) her to marry him.

C.

1. In the past, people (used to dress / used to dressing) more formally than they do now.

2. In the 1940s, my grandmother (used to wear / wore) a skirt to work every day.

3. She also (wouldn't leave / didn't leave) her house without a matching hat and purse.

4. She (wouldn't wear / didn't wear) flat shoes with skirts.

5. She (used to walk / walked) everywhere in heels.

6. My grandfather (used to go / went) to work in a suit every day.

7. He (would work / worked) in the office from 8:00 till 6:00 five days a week.

8. Until the 1960s, most people (didn't use to go / use to not go) outside without a hat.

Practice

Look at the chart about the business world in the 1930s and the business world today. Write sentences about the 1930s with *used to* or *would* (or *didn't use to / wouldn't*) compared with today. Use the verbs in the chart.

	Businesspeople in the Past	Businesspeople Today
1.	type or write by hand	write on computers
2.	work only in the office	work from anywhere (like home)
3.	don't have good phone service	talk on cell phones with improved technology
4.	do a lot of business in person	don't always meet the people they do business with
5.	write letters	send and receive email
6.	don't dress informally	often wear informal clothes

1. _____ ,

but now _____ .

2. Today, _____ ,

but in the past, _____ .

3. _____ ,

but these days _____ .

4. Now, _____ ;

in contrast, in the past, _____ .

5. _____ ;

however, today _____ .

6. These days, _____ ,

whereas in the past, _____ .

17 Practice

Do you see any changes from the recent past until now? Think about the 1980s or the 1990s. What did you use to do then that you don't do now? What would other people do? Write eight sentences with *used to* and *would*. Use the following verbs and your own ideas.

1. listen to / dance to

   _____.

2. pay

   _____.

3. go

   _____.

4. like

   _____.

5. wear

   _____.

6. think

   _____.

7. *your idea*

   _____.

8. *your idea*

   _____.

9. *your idea*

   _____.

10. *your idea*

    _____.

SELF-TEST

A **Choose the best answer, A, B, C, or D, to complete the sentence. Mark your answer by darkening the oval with the same letter.**

1. Maria failed the test. She _____ for it.

   A. didn't use to study   Ⓐ Ⓑ Ⓒ Ⓓ
   B. wasn't studying
   C. hadn't studied
   D. wasn't used to studying

2. While the children _____, the parents relaxed.

   A. had played   Ⓐ Ⓑ Ⓒ Ⓓ
   B. were playing
   C. used to play
   D. would play

3. Amy _____ at a restaurant, but now she works in an office.

   A. was used to working   Ⓐ Ⓑ Ⓒ Ⓓ
   B. use to work
   C. would work
   D. used to work

4. How many miles _____ in that old car?

   A. had he driven   Ⓐ Ⓑ Ⓒ Ⓓ
   B. he drove
   C. had he been driving
   D. he was driving

5. By the time the airplane landed, the passengers _____ for ten hours.

   A. flew   Ⓐ Ⓑ Ⓒ Ⓓ
   B. had been flying
   C. were flying
   D. would fly

6. What TV show _____ last night?

   A. have they watched   Ⓐ Ⓑ Ⓒ Ⓓ
   B. did they watch
   C. had they watched
   D. they were watching

7. The mother did everything she could, but her baby _____ crying.

   A. wouldn't stop   Ⓐ Ⓑ Ⓒ Ⓓ
   B. didn't use to stop
   C. hadn't stopped
   D. wasn't stopping

8. The family was eating breakfast when somebody _____ at the door.

   A. was knocking   Ⓐ Ⓑ Ⓒ Ⓓ
   B. had been knocking
   C. knocked
   D. had knocked

9. How long _____ by the time I got home?

   A. were you waiting   Ⓐ Ⓑ Ⓒ Ⓓ
   B. did you wait
   C. did you use to wait
   D. had you been waiting

10. Tim: Were you talking to me?
    John: No, I _____. I was talking to Bob.

    A. didn't   Ⓐ Ⓑ Ⓒ Ⓓ
    B. wasn't
    C. hadn't
    D. wouldn't

B **Find the underlined word or phrase, A, B, C, or D, that is incorrect. Mark your answer by darkening the oval with the same letter.**

1. I <u>drink</u> coffee <u>these days</u>, but I <u>didn't</u>
      A   B   C

   <u>used to</u>.
    D

   Ⓐ Ⓑ Ⓒ Ⓓ

2. <u>While</u> the woman <u>had been</u> <u>leaving</u> her
    A   B   C

   house, the telephone <u>rang</u>.
                     D

   Ⓐ Ⓑ Ⓒ Ⓓ

3. Before she <u>became</u> a dentist, Lisa <u>had</u>
              A   B

   <u>been</u> <u>being</u> an ice skater.
    C   D

   Ⓐ Ⓑ Ⓒ Ⓓ

4. He <u>had</u> <u>been running</u> twelve miles <u>when</u>
      A   B   C

   he suddenly <u>collapsed</u>.
              D

   Ⓐ Ⓑ Ⓒ Ⓓ

5. By the time we <u>were arriving</u>, the train
                   A

   <u>had</u> <u>already</u> <u>left</u> the station.
    B   C   D

   Ⓐ Ⓑ Ⓒ Ⓓ

6. He <u>looked</u> healthy <u>because</u> he
      A   B

   <u>had been exercise</u> <u>regularly</u>.
        C   D

   Ⓐ Ⓑ Ⓒ Ⓓ

7. <u>Why</u> <u>hasn't</u> anyone <u>told us</u> that we <u>needed</u>
    A   B   C   D

   to be there by 3:00?

   Ⓐ Ⓑ Ⓒ Ⓓ

8. The soccer team <u>used to practice</u> six days
                   A

   <u>a week</u> in 1999, <u>but</u> they <u>aren't</u> now.
    B   C   D

   Ⓐ Ⓑ Ⓒ Ⓓ

9. <u>From the moment</u> the race <u>was starting</u>,
         A   B

   the black horse <u>led</u> all <u>the others</u>.
                 C   D

   Ⓐ Ⓑ Ⓒ Ⓓ

10. Her grandparents <u>were</u> <u>used to</u> <u>live</u>
                   A   B   C

    in a house, but now they <u>live</u> in an
                            D

    apartment.

    Ⓐ Ⓑ Ⓒ Ⓓ

UNIT 3 THE FUTURE TENSES

3a *Be Going To* and *Will*

Student Book p. 58

1 Practice

Complete the sentences with the *be going to* or the *will* form of the verbs in parentheses.

A.

Todd: Oh no! I'm sorry. My dog has just eaten the cookies you baked!

Jennifer: Don't worry. I (bake)

    ___I`ll bake___ some more.
           1
    Do you think your dog

    (get) _____ sick
             2
    from eating all those cookies?

Todd: No, he _____. He (eat) _____ everything.
               3   **4**
    But I think I (take) _____ him outside for a walk. He
                 5
    (not, find) _____ anything interesting to eat out there.
             6

Jennifer: I'm afraid your dog (not, be) _____ very happy outside. It's
                      7
    really cold. I think it (snow) _____.
                   8

Todd: I'm sure he (be) _____ fine. He has a lot of fur. That (keep)
                 9
    _____ him warm.
        10

B.

Kathy: (you, add) _____

          ₁

more fruit to the smoothie?

I'm afraid the blender

(break) _____.

          ₂

There is already a lot of fruit in

there.

Rick: The blender (not, break)

_____.

          3

Don't forget, I (be)

_____ a famous chef someday! I know what I'm doing.

      4

Kathy: Yes, but the juice is already at the top of the blender.

It (spill) _____.

      5

Rick: I've been making this recipe for years. I've never had a problem with it before,

and I (not, have) _____ a problem with it now.

      6

Kathy: There (be) _____ a big mess in the kitchen. I'm sure of it.

      7

Rick: Then I (clean) _____ it up for you. Now, I (put)

      8

_____ the lid on. Then I

      9

(turn on) _____ the blender. Are you ready? Stand back!

      10

Practice

A. Read the information from a brochure about yoga classes. Complete the sentences with *be going to* or *will* and verbs from the list.

be	meet
feel	offer
give	see
help	show
learn	teach
make	

Welcome to Yoga Journeys!

On February 6, Yoga Journeys _is going to offer_ a free class for
$\overline{}$
$\quad\quad\quad\quad\quad\quad\quad$ 1

beginning yoga students. The class _____ from 1:00 to
$\quad\quad\quad\quad\quad\quad\quad\quad\quad\quad\quad$ 2

2:30 at the main studio on Linden Avenue. Our master teacher, Donna Bliss,

_____ this class.
$\quad\quad\quad$ 3

In this class, you _____ the basics of yoga positions.
$\quad\quad\quad\quad\quad\quad\quad\quad\quad$ 4

With her gentle and supportive teaching style, Donna also _____
$\quad\quad\quad\quad\quad\quad\quad\quad\quad\quad\quad\quad\quad\quad\quad\quad$ 5

you how to breathe correctly. Because this is an introductory class, she

(not) _____ you do any complicated movements. Don't worry!
$\quad\quad\quad\quad$ 6

Over time, yoga practice _____ you strength and flexibility.
$\quad\quad\quad\quad\quad\quad\quad\quad\quad\quad$ 7

In one class, you probably (not) _____ instant results. But
$\quad\quad\quad\quad\quad\quad\quad\quad\quad\quad\quad$ 8

you _____ more relaxed after just a few minutes of yoga.
$\quad\quad\quad$ 9

Yoga _____ you to concentrate and to focus.
$\quad\quad$ 10

Our society is becoming more stressful, so yoga _____
$\quad\quad\quad\quad\quad\quad\quad\quad\quad\quad\quad\quad\quad\quad\quad\quad$ 11

an increasingly important way to manage stress in the future. Take a break

from stress. Come join us on a yoga journey!

B. Use the prompts to write yes/no and wh- questions. Use the *be going to* or the *will* form of the verb. Then use information from the reading in Part A to write answers.

1. when / Yoga Journeys / offer / a free class

   Question: <u>When is Yoga Journeys going to offer a free class?</u>

   Answer: <u>Yoga Journeys is going to (OR will) offer a free class on</u>

   <u>February 6, from 1:00-2:30.</u>

2. where / the class / meet

   Question: _____?

   Answer: _____.

3. who / teach / the class

   Question: _____?

   Answer: _____.

4. what / you / learn / in this class

   Question: _____?

   Answer: _____.

5. the teacher / make you learn / any complicated movements

   Question: _____?

   Answer: _____.

6. a yoga class / make / you / stronger and more flexible

   Question: _____?

   Answer: _____.

7. you / feel / strong and flexible / after just one class

   Question: _____?

   Answer: _____.

8. how / you / feel / after just a few minutes of yoga

   Question: _____?

   Answer: _____.

9. why / yoga / be / an increasingly important way to manage stress

   Question: _____?

   Answer: _____.

3 Practice

Think of a sport, hobby, or activity that you enjoy. Imagine you are going to offer a free class on this activity. Write six sentences using *be going to* + verb or *will* + verb. Then use the sentences to create a brochure like the one in Practice 2.

1. _____
2. _____
3. _____
4. _____
5. _____
6. _____

3b Time Clauses and Conditional Sentences in the Future

Student Book p. 63

4 Practice

Marco is traveling in Italy. Match the information in column A with the information in column B to make complete sentences from his letter home.

Dear Mom and Dad,

A

___i___ **1.** I can't believe it! When this train stops,

_____ **2.** While I'm traveling to Rome,

_____ **3.** I'm going to leave my backpack at the hotel

_____ **4.** After I check in to my hotel,

_____ **5.** I won't leave Rome

_____ **6.** I'll think of you both

_____ **7.** I'll buy nice gifts for everyone

_____ **8.** Unless I save some money,

_____ **9.** I'm going to take the train to Naples

_____ **10.** I'll write to you again

B

a. until I see the Trevi Fountain.

b. if I have enough money.

c. as soon as I get to Naples.

d. after I spend three days in Rome.

e. I won't be able to afford a ticket to Naples.

f. I'm going to visit the Coliseum.

g. before I go sightseeing in Rome.

h. while I'm eating gelato on the Spanish Steps.

i. I'll be in Rome!

j. I'll write to you about my plans.

5 Practice

Marco's parents are talking about his letter from Italy. Use the prompts to write their questions about Marco's travel plans. Write each question two ways: once with the time or condition clause at the beginning and once with it at the end. Use correct punctuation.

1. What / do / when / arrive / in Rome

   What is Marco going to do when he arrives in Rome?

   When Marco arrives in Rome, what is he going to do?

2. Where / go / after / leave / Rome

   _____

   _____

3. When / write / to us / after / visit / Naples

   _____

   _____

4. What / do / if / spend / all his money

   _____

   _____

5. How / ask for help / if / get lost

   _____

   _____

6. If / become sick / who / call

   _____

   _____

6 Practice

What are your plans for the future? Complete the sentences with a time clause, a condition clause, or a main clause.

1. As soon as I finish school, _____

   _____.

2. If I have enough money, _____

   _____.

3. I won't get a job _____

   _____.

4. Until I improve my English, _____

   _____.

5. Once I get a job, _____

   _____.

6. While I'm living here, _____

   _____.

7. After I've been living here a while, _____

   _____.

8. I'll be very happy _____

   _____.

9. I'll feel sad _____

   _____.

10. Before _____ ,

   _____.

11. _____ if

   _____.

12. When _____ ,

   _____.

7 **Practice**

Complete the sentences with the present progressive or the simple present.

Amy: When (the store, open)

does the store open ?
1

Salesclerk: We (open) _____
2
at 10:00 every day. Can you come

back?

Amy: I can't. It's 9:15 now, and I (start)

_____ work at 9:30.
3

Salesclerk: This evening we (stay) _____

_____ open until
4

7:30 because of the big shoe sale we

(have) _____. Can you come back later today?
5

Amy: No. Today I (leave) _____ town right after work.
6

Salesclerk: The sale (continue) _____ all through the weekend.
7

You could return on Saturday or Sunday.

Amy: Actually, I (go) _____ out of town for the whole
8

weekend.

Salesclerk: I see. What day (come, you) _____ back?
9

Amy: I (return) _____ on Monday. But I've just remembered —
10

I (not, work) _____ that day.
11

(you, still, sell) _____ shoes at 40% off next week?
12

Salesclerk: No, we (not, be) _____. The sale
13

(end) _____ on Monday.
14

Practice

Keiko and Michael are making plans. Use the information to write sentences about their scheduled activities and arrangements. Use the simple present or the present progressive. The time clause may be at the beginning or the end of the sentence.

Around 6:30:	Michael picks Keiko up at home.
At 7:00:	Eat dinner at the Boston Bistro.
At 8:15:	Movie starts.
At 10:00:	Movie ends.
Around 10:15:	Go out for coffee and dessert.
After coffee and dessert:	Drive to a friend's party.
No later than 11:30:	Michael drives Keiko home.
At 8:00 A.M. the next day:	Keiko works.

1. _Michael is picking Keiko up at home around 6:30._

2. _____

3. _____

4. _____

5. _____

6. _____

7. _____

8. _____

3d The Future Progressive Tense

Student Book p. 70

9 ### Practice
Woodland College is having an open house for new students tomorrow. Use the schedule and prompts to write questions and answers about what will be happening at the open house. Use the future progressive tense.

Woodland College Open House Agenda

8:00   Students and parents arrive at the college.

8:30   Students and parents eat a continental breakfast in the cafeteria.

9:00   Students and parents register for open house.

9:30   The president addresses new students and their parents in the auditorium.

10:00   Morning activities start.

11:30   Students give tours of the campus.

12:00   Professors meet with parents and students at lunch to talk about their classes.

1:00   Dr. Linda Hale lectures about the importance of college today.

2:00   Dr. Ed Mesler leads a discussion about choosing a major.

3:00   Kathleen Henry talks about financial aid.

---

1. when / students and parents / arrive at the college

   Question: *When will students and parents be arriving at the college?*

   Answer: *They will be arriving at the college by 8:00.*

2. when / students and parents / eat breakfast

   Question: _____

   Answer: _____

3. when / students and parents / register for the open house

Question: _____

Answer: _____

4. where / the president / address new students

Question: _____

Answer: _____

5. at what time / morning activities / start

Question: _____

Answer: _____

6. who / give tours / of the campus

Question: _____

Answer: _____

7. what / happen / at lunch

Question: _____

Answer: _____

8. what / Dr. Hale / lecture about

Question: _____

Answer: _____

9. what / Dr. Mesler / lead a discussion about

Question: _____

Answer: _____

10. who / talk about / financial aid

Question: _____

Answer: _____

10 Practice

Shiva and his mother are at the Woodland College Open House. Complete their conversation with *will* + base verb or the future progressive of the verbs in parentheses.

Shiva: The campus tour (start)

will be starting in a few minutes.
₁

Mother: Oh, good. I think I (go) _____
₂
on the tour with you.

Shiva: Actually, the schedule says there (be)

_____ two tours at the
₃
same time: one for parents and one for

students.

Mother: Oh, ok. Then I guess I (take) _____ the tour for parents.
₄

Shiva: (you, go) _____ back to work after that? Or
₅

(you, stay) _____ for lunch?
₆

Mother: I thought I would go back to work. But now I think I (stay) _____.
₇

If I miss lunch, I (not, get) _____ a chance to meet your
₈

professors. I'd like to see what professors you (have) _____
₉

in the fall.

Shiva: You don't have to stay. I (tell) _____ you about them when
₁₀

I come home.

Mother: I'd really like to stay. In just a few weeks you (go) _____
₁₁

to classes, and I (not, see) _____ you as often.
₁₂

11 Practice

Imagine that you are planning a vacation for the people in the photograph. Tell them where they will be going and what they will be doing at the following dates and times. Use the future progressive. You may use ideas from the list or your own.

check in to hotel	hike in the Grand Pitons
dine by candlelight	lie on a beach
fly to St. Lucia	miss the snow and cold

1. On Saturday, January 15, you

   _____

   at 8:00 A.M.

2. At 11:30 A.M., _____

   _____ .

3. _____ by this time tomorrow.

4. _____ in the afternoon.

5. In the evening, _____ .

6. _____ at the end of the day.

3e Other Expressions of the Future; The Future in the Past
Student Book p. 74

12 Practice

Complete the sentences using *be to* or *be about to* + the verbs in parentheses.

1. Gabriel Torres (finish)

   is about to finish his latest

   painting.

2. He (paint) _____ the last detail.

3. The painting (be) _____ displayed in a famous art gallery.

4. It (sell) _____ for nearly $50,000.

5. When the painting is sold, the money (help) _____ start an art program for children in New York City.

6. Gabriel (call) _____ his agent and tell him the good news.

7. His agent thinks Gabriel's art career (become) _____ very successful.

13 Practice

Gabriel had just finished his painting when something happened to change his plans. Complete the sentences using *was/were about to* + the verbs in parentheses.

1. Gabriel (paint) _____ the last part when he heard a noise outside.

2. His five-year-old daughter (knock) _____ on the door, but instead, she ran into the room.

3. Gabriel (move) _____ away from the painting. However, surprised by his daughter, he moved toward it. Red paint sprayed on the canvas.

4. His daughter (laugh) _____, but when she saw Gabriel's face, she started to cry.

5. Gabriel's wife came in. She and Gabriel (yell) _____ at their daughter, but they hugged her instead.

6. They (tell) _____ her that she had done something wrong, but they realized she was too young to understand.

7. Gabriel (call) _____ the agent and tell him the painting would not be done, but then he changed his mind.

8. He (start) _____ a new painting, but then he decided that the red paint made the painting more interesting.

14 Practice

For each photo, write three sentences using the prompts and a verb of your choice.

A.

1. (*be to* or *be about to*)

_____

_____

_____ .

2. (*was/were going to* + verb)

_____ .

3. (*plan, intend, decide,* or *mean* + infinitive)

_____ .

B.

1. (*be to* or *be about to*)

_____

_____

_____

_____ .

2. (*was/were going to* + verb)

_____

_____ .

_____ .

3. (*plan, intend, decide,* or *mean* + infinitive)

_____ .

3f The Future Perfect Tense and The Future Perfect Progressive Tense

Student Book p. 77

15 Practice

Melissa is about to graduate. Complete the sentences using the simple present, the future perfect, or the future perfect progressive and the verbs in parentheses.

1. By the end of the day, Melissa (graduate) _will have graduated_ .

2. By the end of the ceremony, her parents (see) _____ her receive her diploma.

3. Before she (graduate) _____, she

   (practice) _____ the ceremony with her classmates twice.

4. By the end of the ceremony, she (wear) _____

   her cap and gown for two hours.

5. By Sunday, Melissa (attend) _____

   three graduation parties.

6. Also by then, she (receive) _____

   many cards and gifts.

7. Who (her, send) _____ cards

   and gifts?

8. She has many relatives from far away. They (not, come) _____

   _____ by then.

9. By the time she (start) _____ the fall semester at college,

   she (be) _____ away from high school for four months.

10. She (work) _____ for four months before she

    (go) _____ to college.

11. Before she (quit) _____ her summer job, she (save)

_____ her money for college for four months.

12. Hopefully, she (save) _____ at least $1,000 by the end of August.

13. Meanwhile, by this time next year, what (her parents, do) _____ ?

14. They (prepare) _____ for another graduation.

15. Her younger sister (finish) _____ high school by May of next year!

|16| Practice

Imagine that you will live to be 100. What do you think you will have done (or not done) by your 100th birthday? Write three sentences using the future perfect and three sentences using the future perfect progressive.

_____

_____

_____

_____

_____

_____

_____

|17| Practice

Read these sentences about the future. Write _C_ next to the sentence if the tense is used correctly. Write _I_ if it is used incorrectly.

_____ **1.** How long they will have been traveling in Asia?

_____ **2.** By the end of the summer, my little brother will have been reading 25 books.

_____ **3.** Where will everyone be working after the company closes?

_____ **4.** The mayor is give a speech at 3:00 today.

_____ **5.** Jacob will be attending law school next year.

_____ **6.** Will you be being at home tonight, or are you going out?

_____ **7.** If the painters will have finished by 4:00, they will earn more money.

_____ **8.** The boss won't call you unless there is a problem.

_____ **9.** I am about to call her, but I couldn't find the phone number.

_____ **10.** Elise will have practicing the piano for three hours by the time her parents come home.

SELF-TEST

A   Choose the best answer, A, B, C, or D, to complete the sentence. Mark your answer by darkening the oval with the same letter.

1. I will read the book when I _____ the time.

   A. am going to have   Ⓐ Ⓑ Ⓒ Ⓓ
   B. will have
   C. have
   D. am having

2. Hurry up! The class _____ in five minutes!

   A. starts   Ⓐ Ⓑ Ⓒ Ⓓ
   B. will have started
   C. starting
   D. will starting

3. Miguel _____ by the time his brother starts high school.

   A. graduated   Ⓐ Ⓑ Ⓒ Ⓓ
   B. will graduating
   C. will has graduated
   D. will have graduated

4. They _____ that car, but they decided not to.

   A. are going to buy   Ⓐ Ⓑ Ⓒ Ⓓ
   B. are about to buy
   C. will be buying
   D. were about to buy

5. Tom: Oh, no! I left my books in the restaurant.
   Lisa: Wait here. _____ them for you.
   A. I get   Ⓐ Ⓑ Ⓒ Ⓓ
   B. I'll get
   C. I'm going to get
   D. I'm getting

6. Chris has been driving without a break. He _____ in Ohio by 6:00.

   A. is going to arrive   Ⓐ Ⓑ Ⓒ Ⓓ
   B. will arrived
   C. arrives
   D. will arriving

7. Who _____ if you need money?

   A. will you have called   Ⓐ Ⓑ Ⓒ Ⓓ
   B. you will call
   C. will you call
   D. are you calling

8. The neighbors _____ back from vacation until Sunday.

   A. aren't coming   Ⓐ Ⓑ Ⓒ Ⓓ
   B. are not come
   C. not be coming
   D. aren't going to come

9. By the time Sara _____ the gym, she will have been exercising for two hours.

   A. is leaving   Ⓐ Ⓑ Ⓒ Ⓓ
   B. has left
   C. will have left
   D. leaves

10. I can't meet you at 1:00. _____ lunch with my boss at that time.

   A. I'm eat   Ⓐ Ⓑ Ⓒ Ⓓ
   B. I'll be eating
   C. I will have eaten
   D. I will have been eating

B **Find the underlined word or phrase, A, B, C, or D, that is incorrect. Mark your answer by darkening the oval with the same letter.**

1. Jessica <u>is saving</u> all her money <u>because</u>
   A   B

   she <u>will plan</u> <u>to travel</u> in Europe.
        C   D

   Ⓐ Ⓑ Ⓒ Ⓓ

2. <u>Will</u> she <u>has</u> <u>finished</u> the test <u>by the end</u>
   A   B   C   D

   of the class?

   Ⓐ Ⓑ Ⓒ Ⓓ

3. Emily <u>was about to</u> <u>buying</u> the shoes, but
          A   B

   she <u>decided</u> they <u>were</u> too expensive.
       C   D

   Ⓐ Ⓑ Ⓒ Ⓓ

4. The invitation <u>says</u> that the wedding
                   A

   <u>will to</u> <u>begin</u> at <u>exactly</u> 6:00.
    B   C   D

   Ⓐ Ⓑ Ⓒ Ⓓ

5. <u>By the time</u> the baseball game <u>ends</u>, we
   A   B

   <u>will</u> have <u>been spending</u> all our money.
   C   D

   Ⓐ Ⓑ Ⓒ Ⓓ

6. They <u>start</u> the meeting <u>as soon as</u>
        A   B

   everyone <u>has</u> <u>arrived</u>.
            C   D

   Ⓐ Ⓑ Ⓒ Ⓓ

7. <u>What</u> does Ken <u>want</u> to do <u>if</u> he
   A   B   C

   <u>will become</u> president of the club?
    D

   Ⓐ Ⓑ Ⓒ Ⓓ

8. The bus <u>is departing</u> at 9:00 <u>every</u>
            A   B

   morning, and <u>it</u> <u>returns</u> at 3:00 each
                C   D

   afternoon.

   Ⓐ Ⓑ Ⓒ Ⓓ

9. <u>How long</u> <u>they will</u> have <u>been talking</u> by
   A   B   C

   the time they <u>hang up</u> the phone?
                 D

   Ⓐ Ⓑ Ⓒ Ⓓ

10. I <u>predict</u> they <u>are canceling</u> the game <u>if</u>
      A   B   C

    the rain <u>continues</u> all afternoon.
             D

    Ⓐ Ⓑ Ⓒ Ⓓ

UNIT 4 NOUNS AND EXPRESSIONS OF QUANTITY

4a Regular and Irregular Plural Nouns

Student Book p. 90

1 Practice

Complete the sentences with the correct form of the nouns in parentheses.

Yesterday, Daryl took his family to the beach, and they had a great time. There were

(person) _____ playing Frisbee, some (man) _____ were fishing, and
       1   2

lots of (child) _____ were playing in the sand. The (wave) _____
          3   4

weren't very big, so there were no (surfer) _____ in the water. Daryl's family sat
                                          5

in their beach (chair) _____ and laid on their (towel) _____. After a
                      6   7

while, Daryl and his wife walked in the water and got their (foot) _____ wet.
                                                    8

Near the water, some (dog) _____ were chasing some snowy plovers, which are
                                    9

a kind of bird. They are an endangered (species) _____.
                                            10

2 Practice

Read the newscast. Circle the correct form of the verbs in parentheses.

In the news today, five people (was / were)
                              1

caught trying to break in to a department store

downtown. One woman (was / were) later released,
                           2

but the four men (was / were) held at the police
                     3

station. The men (is / are) accused of trying to steal
                 4

radios, CD players, and laptops. The laptops

(was / were) found in the back of the men's van.
  5

The thieves (hasn't / haven't) spoken to lawyers yet.
     6

3 Practice

Read these sentences. Write *C* next to the sentence if the noun forms are correct. Write *I* if the noun forms are incorrect.

———— **1.** Doug is studying physics at school.

———— **2.** When he gets his master's degree, he'll have to write a theses.

———— **3.** He chose that school because it has the best curriculum.

———— **4.** The person in his department are brilliant.

———— **5.** Doug received a memoranda yesterday about his final project.

———— **6.** He's writing a series of articles for a national magazine.

———— **7.** His wife is also a scientist. She studies bacteria in cacti and fungus.

———— **8.** They have a young children.

———— **9.** Their son just got his first tooth.

———— **10.** Doug and his wife hope to get good paying job when they finish their degrees.

4 Practice

Complete the sentences with your own words. Use *is* or *are* in your answers.

1. My teeth _____.

2. The media in my country _____,

so the news _____.

3. _____ an endangered species in my country.

4. Blue jeans _____.

5. Businesspeople _____.

6. A 60-year-old man _____.

7. Five-year-old children _____.

4b Possessive Nouns; Possessive Phrases with *Of*

Student Book p. 93

5 Practice

Read the sentences. Answer the questions with *one* or *more than one*.

1. **a.** The men's hobbies are expensive.
   How many men have hobbies?

   more than one

   b. The man's hobbies are expensive.
   How many men have hobbies?

   _____

2. **a.** The room's furniture needs replacing.
   How many rooms should get new furniture?

   _____

   b. The rooms' furniture needs replacing.
   How many rooms should get new furniture?

   _____

3. **a.** I can't find the child's toys.
   How many children are missing toys?

   _____

   b. I can't find the children's toys.
   How many children are missing toys?

   _____

4. **a.** The boys' projects are almost finished.
   How many boys are almost finished?

   _____

   b. The boy's projects are almost finished.
   How many boys are almost finished?

   _____

5. **a.** The baby's blankets are dirty.
   How many babies have dirty blankets?

   _____

   b. The babies' blankets are dirty.
   How many babies have dirty blankets?

   _____

6. **a.** The students' homework is too difficult.
   How many students have difficult homework?

   _____

   b. The student's homework is too difficult.
   How many students have difficult homework?

   _____

6 Practice

Read the conversations. Rewrite sentence B, adding the possessive noun that is missing.

1. **A:** Whose CD is that?

   B. It's Scott's. <u>It's Scott's CD</u>.

2. **A:** Whose car is that?

   B: It's Leslie's. _____.

3. **A:** Whose responsibility will it be?

   B: It'll be the city's. _____.

4. **A:** Whose turn is it to pay for lunch?

   B: It's Cheryl's. _____.

5. **A:** Whose idea was it to put salt in the sugar bowl?

   B: It was Alex's. _____.

6. **A:** Whose locker was broken into?

   B: Patricia's. _____.

7. **A:** Whose material are you using?

   B: The department's. _____.

8. **A:** Whose database will we be accessing?

   B: Accounting's. _____.

7 Practice

Use apostrophes or *of* and the words in parentheses to complete the sentences.

My (neighbor, house) _____ caught on fire last night.
                            1

The fire started (in the front, house) _____. The
                                            2

(electrical system, house) _____ was faulty. My neighbor
                                3

lost (her mother, jewelry) _____ and (her children,
                                4

photos) _____, but thankfully no one was hurt.
              5

Practice

Read these sentences. Write *C* next to the sentence if the apostrophe or *of* is correct.
Write *I* if it is incorrect.

_____ **1.** Tomorrow homework is to read chapter two.

_____ **2.** We will hear Maria presentation.

_____ **3.** Let's look at today assignment.

_____ **4.** The date of the exam will be announced next week.

_____ **5.** The name the next unit is Ancient Greek History.

_____ **6.** IT installed the laser jet printer in the corner of the room.

_____ **7.** Has Mr. Monroe turned in his letter resignation?

_____ **8.** The erosion hillside is now threatening the subdivisions below it.

9 **Practice**

Write sentences using apostrophes or *of*, the words in parentheses, and your ideas.

1. The (name, this book) is _____.

_The name of this book is Grammar Form and Function_____.

2. My (best friend, name) is _____.

_____.

3. My (parent, taste) in clothes is _____.

_____.

4. My (instructor, name) is _____.

_____.

5. My (family, last vacation) was _____.

_____.

6. The (streets, my city) are _____.

_____.

7. _____ is my favorite (time, the year).

_____.

8. _____ is the (name, my favorite book).

_____.

Compound Nouns

Student Book p. 97

10 Practice

Match each group of words on the left with the word on the right that fits to make compound nouns.

1. _____ : hat, cut, doll   **a.** water
2. _____ : spray, brush, cut   **b.** car
3. _____ : bulb, switch, pole   **c.** music
4. _____ : graphics, programmer, science   **d.** coffee
5. _____ : mechanic, door, seat   **e.** light
6. _____ : fall, glass, bottle   **f.** paper
7. _____ : lesson, teacher, video   **g.** hair
8. _____ : table, pot, machine   **h.** computer

11 Practice

Complete the sentences with compound nouns using the information.

1. The tour was three hours long. It was a _three-hour tour_____ .

2. The girl is seven years old. She's a _____ .

3. The semester is 15 weeks long. It's a _____ .

4. Her latest book is 600 pages long. It is a _____ .

5. The flight was 16 hours long. It was a _____ .

6. The meal was three courses. It was a _____ .

7. The bottle of wine cost six dollars. It was a _____ .

8. Our final paper is going to be ten pages long. It's going to be a _____ .

9. We don't have school on Monday. Our weekend will be three days long. It's going to

   be a _____ .

10. That restaurant has four stars. It must be good. It's a _____ .

12 Practice

Underline the compound nouns in the following reading.

Nick had wanted to be a race-car driver ever since he was a seven-year-old boy. In high school, he worked part time as an auto mechanic while he took driving lessons. The day he got his driver's license was the happiest one of his life!

Nick bought an old car and worked on it in his spare time. He started racing other boys on country roads outside town. As he won more and more of these races, he became more and more confident. Pretty soon, Nick applied to drive on a professional racetrack.

The day of the race, there was a rainstorm. Huge thunderclouds made the sky black, and the race was cancelled. Nick was disappointed, but he now had a chance to double-check his car. It was a good thing. During his inspection, he noticed his seatbelt wasn't connected well to the base! If he had raced, it could have been very dangerous.

◆ 4d Count Nouns and Noncount Nouns

Student Book p. 100

13 Practice

Read these phrases. Write _C_ next to the phrase if the article is used correctly. Write _I_ if it is used incorrectly.

_____ **1.** a happiness

_____ **2.** an air

_____ **3.** an experience

_____ **4.** a weather

_____ **5.** an iron

_____ **6.** a glass

_____ **7.** a sunshine

_____ **8.** two sodas

_____ **9.** a hair

_____ **10.** a rice

14 Practice

Read the recipe for brownies. Circle the count nouns. Underline the noncount nouns.

from the kitchen of _____

Brownies

1 teaspoon vanilla

$\frac{1}{2}$ cup butter

$\frac{3}{4}$ cup flour

2 squares of chocolate

$\frac{1}{2}$ cup nuts

1 cup of sugar

2 eggs

Melt the butter and chocolate together. Remove from heat. Stir in sugar. Add eggs and vanilla. Mix gently until combined. Add flour and nuts. Put mixture in a square cake pan and bake for 30 minutes at 350°.

15 Practice

Circle the correct verbs in parentheses.

1. Geography (isn't / aren't) very interesting to me.

2. Medicine (is / are) a popular major at my university.

3. My new glasses (is / are) already broken!

4. Bad experiences (is / are) a part of life.

5. Chocolate (is / are) good for you.

6. Education (is / are) very important.

7. The good times I had in college (was / were) some of my happiest moments.

8. Time (goes / go) quickly.

9. Gasoline (has been / have been) very expensive lately.

10. The two cups of coffee I had this morning (is / are) making me nervous.

16 Practice

Add two more items to each of the noncount noun lists.

Languages	Natural Forces	Recreation
Portuguese	*wind*	*soccer*
_____	_____	_____
_____	_____	_____

Abstract Nouns	Liquid	Particles
love	*milk*	*sand*
_____	_____	_____
_____	_____	_____

17 Practice

Complete the sentences with *much, many, little,* or *few*.

A. Art Director: You don't have _____ ideas.

1

    Artist: I didn't have _____ time to do this. _____

2   3

    artists could meet this deadline. I had _____ warning.

4

    Art Director: This is an important client. _____ other companies want

5

    its business.

B. Mia: My parrot isn't doing _____ talking today.

1

    Tawni: Do you think he's depressed? He has very _____ room to walk

2

    around in that cage.

    Mia: No, this is just his traveling cage. His cage at home is huge.

    _____ birds have such luxury!

3

    Tawni: Oh, so where's he going?

    Mia: To my best friend's apartment. He's gone there _____ times

4

    before. He loves to go visit, so he'll probably start talking again once we

    get there.

18 Practice

Complete the sentences with your own ideas.

1. Students have too much _____ and too little _____.

2. They have too many _____ and too few _____.

3. Parents have too many _____ and too few _____.

4. In the winter, there is too much _____ and too little _____.

4e *Some* and *Any*

Student Book p. 103

19 Practice

Circle the correct words in parentheses.

Leonard: Come on over. We can get (some / any) Chinese food.
                                                    1

Ziggy: There's never (some / any) parking in your neighborhood.
                                      2

Leonard: Take the bus. There isn't (some / any) traffic this time of day.
                                                    3

Ziggy: Okay. Should I bring (some / any) drinks?
                                            4

Leonard: Well, I have (some / any) bananas and yogurt and was thinking of making
                                  5

               (some / any) smoothies.
                        6

Ziggy: Okay. How about if I bring (some / any) strawberries? Oh, and I've also got
                                                      7

               (some / any) new CDs to show you.
                        8

Leonard: Great.

20 Practice

Read these sentences. Write *C* next to the sentence if *some* or *any* is used correctly. Write *I* if it is used incorrectly.

_____ **1.** The team finished the project without some problems.

_____ **2.** The kids still have some homework to do.

_____ **3.** Dr. Walker seldom has any time for hobbies.

_____ **4.** Darlene's lost weight. She hardly has some clothes to wear.

_____ **5.** She needs to buy some new shoes, too.

_____ **6.** We have to water the garden because we haven't had some rain.

_____ **7.** If you have your own business, you rarely take some vacations.

_____ **8.** You can wear my sunglasses. I have any extra ones in the car.

21 Practice

Complete the sentences with *some* if the speaker expects a "yes" answer. Complete the sentences with *any* if the speaker has no expectation.

1. (I need tape, but I don't know if you have tape.)

Do you have ___any___ tape?

2. (I think you'll let me borrow money.)

Could I borrow _____ money?

3. (Your friend is having a party. You think she needs help.)

Do you need _____ help?

4. (You don't know if your friend has enough food for the party.)

Should I bring _____ snacks?

5. (You don't know if other people from work are going to be at the party.)

Will _____ people from work be there?

6. (Your friend doesn't have enough CDs. You think she would like music at the party.)

Do you want me to bring _____ music?

22 Practice

Write *a, b,* or *c* beside each sentence to identify which meaning of *any* is being used.

———— **1.** I can meet you any time you like.

———— **2.** There's hardly any tea left!

———— **3.** Our math teacher doesn't have any patience.

———— **4.** Any kind of cake is fine with me.

———— **5.** Are there any more dishes in the sink?

———— **6.** She never has any money.

———— **7.** Did you have any pets growing up?

———— **8.** Jake will take any job he's offered.

a. Negative meaning

b. No expectation

c. It doesn't matter which one

4f *Much, Many, A Lot Of, A Few, Few, A Little,* and *Little*

Student Book p. 106

23 Practice

Complete the sentences with *a little, a few,* or *a lot of.* More than one answer may be correct.

Anne: My wallet was stolen!

Mike: Did you have _____
                                    1
money in it?

Anne: No, only _____, but I had
                              2
_____ pictures and credit
              3
cards.

Mike: When did this happen?

Anne: Only _____ hours ago.
                        4

Mike: Have you called the police?

Anne: Yes, I talked to them _____ while ago.
                                              5

Mike: Do you need _____ money right now? I can lend you some.
                                6

Anne: No, thanks, Mike. I have _____ dollars at home.
                                                7

24 Practice

Complete the sentences with *much, many, a few, few, a little, little,* or *a lot of*.

My nephew is staying with me for the summer, and he's driving me crazy. We're having

_____ problems, not many. He tried doing his laundry and put too
          1

_____ soap in the washing machine. There were bubbles and water everywhere!
          2

He gets too _____ phone calls late at night, and he makes too
                      3

_____ noise. I'm getting very _____ sleep. I still have
          4   5

_____ patience, but I'm left with _____ options. _____
          6   7   8

things are going to have to change.

25 Practice

What does each sentence mean? Answer the questions.

1. I have a few friends.

   Do I have friends? <u>Yes, you have some friends, but not a lot of friends</u>.

2. My brother has few friends.

   Does he have friends? _____.

3. The students have very little time to finish the project.

   How much time do the students have? _____.

4. Very few people are still in the office at this hour.

   How many people are still working? _____.

5. There's a little soap left.

   Can I do laundry? _____.

6. We found a little money in the sofa!

   How much money did they find? _____.

7. The director has made few changes to the proposal.

   Has the proposal been changed a lot? _____.

8. We're having a few friends over for dinner.

   How many people will be at dinner? _____.

4g Each, Each (One) Of, Every, Every One Of, Both, Both Of, All, and All Of

Student Book p. 110

26 Practice

Katie bought a new PDA two months ago. Read the paragraph and circle the correct expressions in parentheses.

    I have trouble with this thing (each / every)¹ day. (Each / Every)² time I use it, I have to restart it. I have spoken to two customer service representatives, and (each / every)³ one has told me something different! My husband has the same machine, and (all of / both of)⁴ us are frustrated. (All / Every)⁵ my friends love their PDAs and never have any problems with them. Today mine crashed, and I can't access the information. (Every one of / Each)⁶ my addresses is in it. I think I'm going to return (all of / both of)⁷ ours to the store.

27 Practice

Complete the sentences with *both*, *every*, or *all*.

1. Sharon's been to that doctor twice. _____ times, he's kept her waiting for an hour.

2. _____ time she tries to talk to him, he's busy.

3. He laughed at _____ my jokes, and I told him a lot of them.

4. _____ meal on the menu was too expensive.

5. Our daughter's pet hamster kept us awake _____ night.

6. Luanne can write with _____ hands.

7. When Juan won the lottery, _____ of his money problems disappeared.

8. _____ Alan and Jan have agreed to sign the petition.

9. _____ one of the people in that room was angry.

10. _____ the exercises in the book are easy.

28 Practice
Complete the sentences with your own ideas.

1. Both of my eyes _____.

2. Both of my parents _____.

3. All of my friends _____.

4. Each one of my teachers _____.

5. Every one of my classmates _____.

6. Both of my shoes _____.

7. All children _____.

8. Every newspaper in my country _____.

9. Every person needs _____.

10. All of the people in the world _____.

SELF-TEST

A Choose the best answer, A, B, C, or D, to complete the sentence. Mark your answer by darkening the oval with the same letter.

1. My aunt never had any _____.

   A. childs   Ⓐ Ⓑ Ⓒ Ⓓ
   B. child's
   C. children's
   D. children

2. When Matthew was in high school, mathematics _____ his favorite subject.

   A. was   Ⓐ Ⓑ Ⓒ Ⓓ
   B. were
   C. are
   D. is

3. Last ____ fashions were influenced by hip-hop.

   A. year   Ⓐ Ⓑ Ⓒ Ⓓ
   B. year's
   C. years
   D. of year

4. The neighbors bought a _____ house.

   A. 100-year-old   Ⓐ Ⓑ Ⓒ Ⓓ
   B. 100-years-old
   C. 100-year's-old
   D. 100-year

5. Pollution in the city _____ in recent years.

   A. are decreased   Ⓐ Ⓑ Ⓒ Ⓓ
   B. have decreased
   C. has decreased
   D. were decreased

6. There weren't _____ people injured at the concert.

   A. much   Ⓐ Ⓑ Ⓒ Ⓓ
   B. any
   C. some
   D. few

7. My country has very ____ iron, so we import it.

   A. much   Ⓐ Ⓑ Ⓒ Ⓓ
   B. many
   C. little
   D. few

8. We rarely get ____ rain in the summer here.

   A. much   Ⓐ Ⓑ Ⓒ Ⓓ
   B. many
   C. little
   D. few

9. David works out _____ day.

   A. all of   Ⓐ Ⓑ Ⓒ Ⓓ
   B. every
   C. each
   D. both

10. We can't bake a cake. We have too ____ sugar.

   A. many   Ⓐ Ⓑ Ⓒ Ⓓ
   B. few
   C. a little
   D. little

B **Find the underlined word or phrase, A, B, C, or D, that is incorrect. Mark your answer by darkening the oval with the same letter.**

1. We can see some <u>sheep</u>, <u>man</u>, <u>women</u>,
                    A   B   C

   children, and <u>geese</u> in the painting.
                D

   Ⓐ Ⓑ Ⓒ Ⓓ

2. <u>Both of</u> the three plays we saw <u>were</u>
     A   B

   good. The <u>name of one</u> was *The Time of*
              C

   Your Life. It was <u>Ted's</u> favorite.
                   D

   Ⓐ Ⓑ Ⓒ Ⓓ

3. Mollie took her <u>two-year-old</u> twins on a
                       A

   <u>five-hour</u> trip to Boston. <u>Both</u> days that
      B   C

   weekend, she didn't get <u>some</u> rest.
                    D

   Ⓐ Ⓑ Ⓒ Ⓓ

4. Al has a <u>driver's license</u>, so he's taking us
            A

   to the <u>bookstore</u>. First, I need to get
        B

   <u>a little</u> money. We don't have <u>few</u> time.
     C   D

   Ⓐ Ⓑ Ⓒ Ⓓ

5. They didn't have <u>any</u> oranges at the store,
              A

   so I got <u>some</u> bananas. I also got <u>a few</u>
         B   C

   cheese and <u>a little</u> juice.
            D

   Ⓐ Ⓑ Ⓒ Ⓓ

6. <u>Each people</u> must have a ticket. You
     A

   cannot use another <u>person's</u> ticket, but
                B

   you can use the same ticket <u>all</u> day. Let's
                        C

   go over <u>a few</u> rules.
         D

   Ⓐ Ⓑ Ⓒ Ⓓ

7. Athletics <u>is</u> an important part of school.
         A

   <u>Every</u> <u>student</u> should do <u>few</u> exercise.
     B   C   D

   Ⓐ Ⓑ Ⓒ Ⓓ

8. I'm washing <u>jeans</u>, <u>short</u>, and <u>pajamas</u>.
            A   B   C

   There's <u>a little</u> hot water if you need to
          D

   take a shower.

   Ⓐ Ⓑ Ⓒ Ⓓ

9. We had a <u>four-hour</u> dinner. <u>Each of us</u> had
           A   B

   fun, and we told a <u>lot of</u> jokes, but I
                 C

   don't remember the <u>name's restaurant</u>.
                   D

   Ⓐ Ⓑ Ⓒ Ⓓ

10. Many <u>exercises</u> in this book <u>is</u> easy, and
        A   B

    <u>a few</u> exercises <u>are</u> fun.
      C   D

    Ⓐ Ⓑ Ⓒ Ⓓ

UNIT 5 PRONOUNS AND ARTICLES

5a Subject and Object Pronouns; Possessive Adjectives; and Possessive Pronouns

Student Book p. 120

☐1 Practice

Circle the correct subject, object, possessive pronoun, or possessive adjective.

A. Rich and Sue are discussing their wedding reception.

Sue: Let's put (your / yours) parents next to (my / mine).

                        1   2

Rich: But (my / mine) mother doesn't really know (your / yours).

                3   4

Sue: I know, but I don't know where else to seat (her / hers).

                                        5

B. George Washington Carver was the first African American to graduate from what is now Iowa State University. (He / Him) was responsible for many agricultural innovations and discoveries. One of (them / their) was the invention of peanut butter. No one (know / knows) exactly when (he / him) was born, but it was around 1865. (He / His) parents were slaves.

C. (She / Her) said that (her / hers) soccer team had just won the championship match. The trophy is (their / theirs) for the first time. The team and coaches are already planning for next year. (Them / They) want to be sure that the championship trophy stays with (they / them).

D. A wife and husband have just moved into a new house.

Wife: What's (our / ours) new phone number?

                          1

Husband: It's 555-8765.

Wife: No, it's not. That's (our / ours) old one.

                                 2

2 Practice

Complete the sentences with possessive adjectives or pronouns *(my, mine, her, hers, his, our, ours, their, theirs).*

A. Sarah: I don't want any dessert. You can have _____.
                                                                    1

   Ryan: Thanks, but I think _____ dessert is going to be enough.
                                              2

B. Jenna Lee has just had a job interview. The interviewers are discussing her.

   Donna: What did you think of the candidate?

   Leroy: _____ ideas are interesting.
            1

   Donna: Do you think _____ are better than the other candidates' ideas?
                            2

   Leroy: Yes, I do, but I'm not sure we can offer _____ enough money to
                                                       3

           leave _____ other job.
                   4

C. Maureen: When does _____ vacation start?

   Jorge: We leave next Saturday.

D. Two children are arguing over a toy.

   Pete: Give it back! It's _____.
                                  1

   Ken: No, it's not! It's _____.
                                2

   Mom: Ken! Give it to Pete. It's _____.
                                         3

E. Candace and Joyce have _____ own business.

F. Several people are in the reception area of a public relations firm. The new receptionist

   goes to ask whose clients they are.

   Receptionist: Can anyone tell me whose clients are waiting in reception?

   Margo and Miriam: The client in the red suit is _____ client. And the client
                                                      1

                   in the black skirt is Norm and Sara's.

   Norm and Sara: Yes, the client wearing red is _____, and the other one
                                                     2

                   is _____.
                        3

G. We have an exchange student from Sweden. I'm learning _____ language,
                                                               1

   and he's learning _____.
                        2

H. Instructor: Please turn off _____ cell phones.

1

(phone ringing)

Eun Hee: It's not _____. Marc, I think it's _____.

2   3

Marc: Oops! Sorry. Yes, it's _____ phone.

4

3 Practice

**Read about Komodo dragons.
Complete the sentences with
it's or *its*.**

_____ the largest

1

lizard in the world. _____

2

found on two Indonesian islands.

_____ teeth can tear

3

easily through flesh.

_____ mouth is filled with bacteria. The infection from a bite can kill

4

_____ prey. _____ long tongue "tastes" the air. A

5   6

Komodo dragon starts _____ attack when _____ three

7   8

feet away from _____ victim. _____ an interesting,

9   10

but ferocious animal.

4 Practice

Answer the questions with *it*.

1. What time is it? _____.

2. What's the weather like? _____.

3. What's the temperature right now? _____.

4. How far is it from your house to your school? _____.

5. How long does it take you to go to school? _____.

6. What's the weather going to be like tomorrow? _____.

5 Practice

Read these sentences. Write *C* next to the sentence if the pronouns and possessive adjectives are used correctly. Write *I* if they are used incorrectly.

_____ **1.** It's ours.

_____ **2.** The baseball fans forgot his tickets.

_____ **3.** Scott critiqued hers project.

_____ **4.** Someone took my parking space!

_____ **5.** Him's drinking some coffee.

_____ **6.** She loves vacations at the beach.

_____ **7.** Everyone needs to bring his or her lunch.

_____ **8.** Talk to she about the plan.

_____ **9.** You can look for apartments online.

_____ **10.** Vicky bought the tickets for we.

6 Practice

Read the sentences. Write *a* next to the sentence if the pronoun is formal. Write *b* if the pronoun is informal. Write *c* if the pronoun is inappropriate.

_____ **1.** Someone left their lights on.   **a.** formal

_____ **2.** Everyone is required to clean out his or her locker.   **b.** informal

_____ **3.** Did someone call? Did they leave a message?   **c.** inappropriate

_____ **4.** If one has time, one should help others less fortunate.

_____ **5.** A good driver has to pay attention to what he's doing.

_____ **6.** No one should say things they don't mean.

_____ **7.** Everyone should clear his desk now.

_____ **8.** A child needs lots of love and support while he or she is growing up.

_____ **9.** Anyone can go, but they need to make a reservation.

_____ **10.** A good teacher should be sensitive to her students' needs.

5b Reflexive Pronouns

Student Book p. 128

7 Practice

Complete the sentences with the correct reflexive pronouns.

A. If you want something done right, do it _____.

B. Mom: What happened?!

Henry: Freddy and I tried to fix the car by _____. Freddy cut
                                                            1

_____ on a sharp piece of metal, and I burned _____
            2   3

on the exhaust pipe.

Mom: Are you okay?

Henry: Yes, but we can't fix the car _____. We'll take it to a mechanic.
                                                      4

C. Carolina: I'm glad you made
               it to the party!
               Are you enjoying

               _____?
                        1

Aaron: Of course! I didn't
               know anyone here,
               so I introduced

               _____
                        2

               to Zoe and Ian.

Carolina: Great. Be sure to help _____ to some cookies. I made
                                                        3

them _____.
          4

8 Practice

Replace the underlined words and phrases with *by* and appropriate reflexive pronouns.

1. On the first day of school, the young friends said, "We can walk to school <u>alone</u>."

On the first day of school, the young friends said, "We can

walk to school by ourselves."

2. They wanted to walk to school <u>alone</u>.

_____.

3. Some of the most important lessons we learn in life, we have to learn <u>without others</u>.

_____.

4. She's doing this exercise <u>alone</u>.

_____.

5. He doesn't want to go to the party <u>alone</u>.

_____.

6. My three-year-old son wants to get dressed <u>without my help</u>.

_____.

7. I don't like living with roommates. I like living <u>alone</u>.

_____.

8. Victor and Carol are nervous about driving to Florida <u>alone</u>.

_____.

9. You are too dependent on your friends. You should do more things <u>on your own</u>.

_____.

10. Father to his two children: Please, go out to the back yard and play <u>with just you two</u>

for a few minutes. _____.

9 Practice

Read the sentences. Circle the correct reflexive pronoun in each. If it is incorrect, rewrite the sentence.

1. I didn't invite him! He invited him! _____ _He invited himself_ _____.

2. Our daughter wrote us from Mexico. She's enjoying herself. _____.

3. Chen cut himself shaving this morning. _____.

4. It's an all-you-can-eat-buffet. Help yourselves. _____.

5. I me will help you. _____.

6. Our dog taught herself how to open the door to the refrigerator. _____.

7. The accident was our fault. We blame us. _____.

8. The children locked themselves in the bedroom. We had to call the fire department.

_____.

9. Anne promised her to quit smoking. _____.

10. Patrick painted the room him. _____.

10 Practice

Complete the sentences with your own ideas and appropriate reflexive pronouns.

1. <u> I </u> don't take care of <u> *myself* </u> when I <u> *get too busy* </u> .

2. _____ scared _____ when I _____ .

3. _____ surprised _____ when she _____ .

4. _____ doesn't look at _____ in the mirror because

    _____ .

5. _____ talks to _____ when he _____ .

6. _____ drove _____ to the hospital when

    _____ .

5c *Another, Other, Others, The Other,* and *The Others*

Student Book p. 130

11 Practice

Read the sentences. Circle the correct words in parentheses.

1. Some students are coming with us, and (other / others) are meeting us there.

2. Sharon: How's your mom?

    Ron: Some days she's okay, but (other / others) days she's very tired.

3. Jasminda: How long does it take you to get to work?

    Miriam: Most days, just 40 minutes on the subway, but (other / others) days it can take an hour.

4. Walter: I'm looking for an apartment. Can you give me some suggestions?

    Brigitte: Some neighborhoods are pretty nice, but (other / others) are not very safe.

5. Stephanie: How's your new boss?

Paulo: She's okay. Sometimes we work well together, but (other / others) days I don't understand her management style.

6. Flight attendant 1: Your flight was crowded and late arriving to Buenos Aires. How were the passengers?

Flight attendant 2: Some passengers were calm, (other / others) were angry, and (other / others) were confused.

7. Volunteer 1: Where have all the donations come from?

Volunteer 2: Some have come from religious organizations, (other / others) donations have come from schools, and still (other / others) have come from individual people.

12 Practice

Complete the sentences with *the other, the others,* or *another*.

1. Mitch is taking five classes. Two are interesting, but _____ aren't.

2. Our team needs _____ week to finish the project.

3. Duane ate one hamburger, then he ate _____, and

_____, and _____!

4. Denise has two neighbors. One is friendly, but _____ isn't.

5. We need _____ $6,000 to finish the house.

6. The company interviewed eight candidates for the positions. Four of them were overqualified, three didn't have the skills we need, but _____ was perfect for the job.

7. Patricia knew some of the students but not _____.

8. The violinist has released a record a year for the last six years. We have two of them but not _____.

13 Practice

Answer the questions.

1. Underline every other letter.   A B C D E F G H I

2. What's every other day of the week?   Sunday, _____

3. Underline every other year.   1998, 1999, 2000, 2001, 2002, 2003, 2004, 2005, 2006

4. What's every other month in the year? _____

14 Practice

Read these sentences. Write C next to the sentence if *the other, the others, other, others, every other,* or *another* is used correctly. Write I if it is used incorrectly.

———— **1.** We'll be there in the other half an hour.

———— **2.** The players don't get along with each other.

———— **3.** Cost is one reason I can't go to Australia, but there are the others.

———— **4.** Lydia works out every other day.

———— **5.** My mom is one of my heroes, but I have many anothers.

———— **6.** One foot is bigger than the other.

———— **7.** Only 50 guests came to the reception. Some never got their invitations, and others got them late.

———— **8.** Go to bed right now. I don't want to hear another excuse.

5d The Indefinite Articles *A* and *An; One* and *Ones*
Student Book p. 133

15 Practice

Read these sentences. Write C next to the sentence if the article is used correctly. Write I if it is used incorrectly.

———— **1.** What time is it? I don't have watch.

———— **2.** Did we have an assignment for tomorrow?

———— **3.** Does anyone have a cell phone?

———— **4.** I need to make call.

———— **5.** All living things need an air to breathe.

———— **6.** Grapes cost $0.69 a pound.

———— **7.** Bill works out three days week.

———— **8.** Jessie needs a new wallet.

———— **9.** Before the sales department makes decision, they need more information.

———— **10.** I like to have an apple for breakfast in the morning.

16 Practice

Read the paragraph about Joel. Complete the sentences with *a, an,* or *one*.

My nephew, Joel, hasn't had _____ job in over _____ year. He got _____ call today telling him that he has _____ interview on Thursday. Joel needs _____ haircut, _____ new suit, _____ better résumé, and he only has _____ reference. His interview is at 9:00 in the morning, but I'm not sure he has _____ alarm clock. I hope _____ day, he'll be more organized!

1 2 3 4 5 6 7 8 9 10

17 Practice

Rewrite the sentences replacing the repeated nouns with *one* or *ones*. You may need to make other changes to the articles in the sentences.

1. Sharlene: Don, do you want a soda?

   Don: No, thanks. I already have a soda. *No, thanks. I already have one* .

2. My teacher likes the old designs better than the new designs.

   _____ .

3. Vanessa: What's on TV tonight?

   Tom: I don't know. I don't have a TV.

   _____ .

4. Sean: Which car did she get?

   Vicky: She got the red car.

   _____ .

5. My inbox was filled with messages, so I deleted the old messages.

   _____ .

6. Rosa: How was the conference?

Sadiq: It was the worst conference I've ever been to!

_____.

7. Allen: Oh, no! My computer has crashed!

Tyra: Use the computer at the library.

_____.

8. Enrique: How are you doing in your history class?

Tim: Okay. I failed the first test, but passed the other tests.

_____.

9. Salesperson: The earrings on the counter are full price, but the earrings in the basket

are on sale. _____

_____.

18 Practice

Think about your future. Start your sentences with "one day."

1. _One day, I'm going to have a house with a pool_ .

2. _____.

3. _____.

4. _____.

5. _____.

5e The Definite Article *The*

Student Book p. 138

19 Practice

Add *the* to the sentences if necessary. If it's not necessary, don't add anything.

1. Everyone should drink _____ water.

2. _____ water in our city doesn't taste very good.

3. Frank went to _____ store.

4. I got some fruit. Please put _____ bananas on the counter.

5. Ben and his friends are planning a trip to _____ Europe.

6. Look at _____ stars! They're beautiful tonight.

7. Neil Armstrong was _____ first person to walk on _____ moon.

8. My sister's family has a rabbit, a cat, and a dog. _____ rabbit and

_____ dog get along well, but _____ cat doesn't like anyone!

9. Manuel loves _____ animals.

10. _____ animals on our rescue farm get good care.

20

Practice

Read the article about surfing. Cross out *the* whenever it's not necessary.

The surfing originated in the Hawaiian Islands. The first European to record a
___ ___ ___
1 **2** **3**
description of it was the Lieutenant James King. The surfing is called "The Sport of
___ ___ ___
4 **5** **6**
Kings." Hawaiian royalty had beaches and surfboards that were different from everyone

else's. Hawaiian culture had strict rules, but as more and more the Westerners came to
___
7
Hawaii, the traditions and culture changed. The surfing on the Hawaii fell off, but never
___ ___ ___
8 **9** **10**
died out completely. In the 1850s, surfing began to gain in popularity again.
___
11

21 Practice

Complete the sentences with your own ideas.

1. **a.** Japanese is _fun to study_ .

   b. The Japanese are _very polite_ .

2. **a.** People are _____.

   b. The people in my city are _____.

3. **a.** Music is _____.

   b. The music from Jamaica is _____.

4. **a.** Pollution is _____.

   b. The pollution in my city is _____.

5. **a.** Money is _____.

   b. The money in my wallet is _____.

22 Practice

Complete the sentences with *a, an,* or *the*.

1. We're having ___a___ test next week. ___The___ test will cover chapters 6, 7, and 8.

2. I need to get _____ new printer. _____ one I have now is too old.

3. Do you know _____ good babysitter? _____ guy we usually call is busy on Saturday.

4. _____ sun was really hot today! Vince got _____ bad sunburn.

5. Leon has to write _____ book report. I've never heard of _____ book he's chosen.

6. We took _____ taxi yesterday, and I left my sunglasses in _____ cab.

7. Bring _____ sweater with you this weekend. _____ nights can be really cold at our cabin.

8. Rachel had _____ problem with her car. The mechanic says _____ problem is in _____ fuel line.

9. Host: Do you have _____ reservation?

   Guest: Yes, _____ reservation is for 7:00 for four people.

23 Practice

Read the recipe for Easy Fruit Salad. Complete the sentences with *a, an,* or *the*.

Easy Fruit Salad

_____ apple
1

_____ banana
2

_____ orange
3

a few grapes

_____ melon*
4

(* or any other fruit you like)

_____ lemon
5

2 Tablespoons of honey or any
kind of jam

To make the sauce, squeeze _____ lemon into
6

_____ medium-size bowl. Add _____ honey and mix well.
7   8

To make the fruit salad, cut up _____ apple, _____ melon, and
9   10

_____ banana into _____ bowl. Peel _____ orange and
11   12   13

add it and _____ grapes into _____ fruit mixture. Fold
14   15

_____ fruit and sauce gently together and serve!
16

24 Practice

Write a recipe for something you like to make.
Write a list of ingredients and instructions.

_____

_____

_____

_____

_____

_____

A **Choose the best answer, A, B, C, or D, to complete the sentence. Mark your answer by darkening the oval with the same letter.**

1. Everyone has to do _____ own work.

   A. they Ⓐ Ⓑ Ⓒ Ⓓ
   B. their
   C. our
   D. my

2. My family drives me crazy, but I love _____ all.

   A. them Ⓐ Ⓑ Ⓒ Ⓓ
   B. theirs
   C. it
   D. we

3. In order to win the contest, you must complete the task by _____.

   A. myself Ⓐ Ⓑ Ⓒ Ⓓ
   B. yourself
   C. himself
   D. itself

4. The children made the dinner by _____.

   A. ourselves Ⓐ Ⓑ Ⓒ Ⓓ
   B. yourselves
   C. themselves
   D. herself

5. Al and Matt saw a couple of movies this weekend. One was terrible, but _____ was pretty good.

   A. each other Ⓐ Ⓑ Ⓒ Ⓓ
   B. another
   C. the other
   D. other

6. Lisa needs to get _____ job. The one she has now doesn't pay enough.

   A. each other Ⓐ Ⓑ Ⓒ Ⓓ
   B. another
   C. the other
   D. other

7. Naoko's family goes to _____ Netherlands every other year.

   A. an Ⓐ Ⓑ Ⓒ Ⓓ
   B. a
   C. one
   D. the

8. I've got _____ headache.

   A. an Ⓐ Ⓑ Ⓒ Ⓓ
   B. a
   C. one
   D. the

9. _____ speak Korean.

   A. They Koreans Ⓐ Ⓑ Ⓒ Ⓓ
   B. The Koreans
   C. The Koreans people
   D. The people

10. The family took a trip around _____ world.

    A. an Ⓐ Ⓑ Ⓒ Ⓓ
    B. a
    C. one
    D. the

B   Find the underlined word or phrase, A, B, C, or D, that is incorrect. Mark your answer by darkening the oval with the same letter.

1. She's <u>a</u> very skilled manager. She worked
   _A

   <u>hers</u> way up by <u>herself</u>. I model my career
   _B   _C

   on <u>hers</u> because she's so successful.
   _D

   Ⓐ Ⓑ Ⓒ Ⓓ

2. Please, help <u>ourselves</u>. There's plenty of
   _A

   food for <u>everyone</u>. Ursula made <u>her</u>
   _B   _C

   famous cookies. <u>They're</u> delicious.
   _D

   Ⓐ Ⓑ Ⓒ Ⓓ

3. Let's have <u>the other</u> party soon! Everyone
   _A

   had a good time. The guests helped

   <u>themselves</u> to food and introduced
   _B

   <u>themselves</u> to <u>each other</u>.
   _C   _D

   Ⓐ Ⓑ Ⓒ Ⓓ

4. This was <u>a</u> great party! The kids behaved
   _A

   <u>themselves</u> and we enjoyed <u>yourself</u>. <u>Other</u>
   _B   _C   _D

   parties I've been to haven't been much fun.

   Ⓐ Ⓑ Ⓒ Ⓓ

5. I gave <u>herself</u> <u>a</u> headache thinking about
   _A   _B

   it. It's too difficult to solve <u>by myself</u>.
   _C

   I need help from <u>the others</u> on our team.
   _D

   Ⓐ Ⓑ Ⓒ Ⓓ

6. Can you get me <u>another</u> knife? This <u>one</u> is
   _A   _B

   dirty. Steve will be late for <u>the</u> dinner
   _C

   party, but <u>each other</u> will be on time.
   _D

   Ⓐ Ⓑ Ⓒ Ⓓ

7. Jack Campbell bought <u>a</u> tent, <u>a</u> sleeping
   _A   _B

   bag, <u>the</u> ice chest, and <u>a</u> backpack for his
   _C   _D

   camping trip.

   Ⓐ Ⓑ Ⓒ Ⓓ

8. People speak <u>the Portuguese</u> in Brazil,
   _A

   <u>English</u> in Australia, <u>French</u> in France, and
   _B   _C

   <u>Japanese</u> in Japan.
   _D

   Ⓐ Ⓑ Ⓒ Ⓓ

9. Linda has to have <u>the</u> best clothes, <u>a</u>
   _A   _B

   most expensive jewelry, <u>the</u> biggest car,
   _C

   and <u>the</u> nicest house.
   _D

   Ⓐ Ⓑ Ⓒ Ⓓ

10. Michael can play <u>the</u> guitar, <u>the</u> piano,
    _A   _B

    <u>one</u> harmonica, and <u>the flute</u>.
    _C   _D

    Ⓐ Ⓑ Ⓒ Ⓓ

81

UNIT 6 MODALS I

6b *Can, Could,* and *Be Able To* to Express Ability

Student Book p. 151

1 Practice

Complete the sentences with *can, could,* or *be able to* in the correct tense. More than one answer may be possible.

1. Karen: Why didn't you go?

   Jim: I (not) _____ find anyone to take my class.

2. Police officer: How did you escape from the locked room?

   Vince: I _____ reach the window, open it a little, and yell

   for help.

3. Boss: _____ (you) stay late tomorrow?

   Assistant: No, I'm sorry. I (not) _____ stay late.

4. Mark: Darla _____ always get reservations at the best

   sushi restaurant in town.

   Jeff: She's lucky. Whenever I call, I (not) _____

   get a reservation for the day I want.

5. The director _____ see you tomorrow at 10:30 A.M.

6. Seth: How (you) _____ reach the top shelf?

   Anita: I _____ reach the top shelf by standing on a

   dining room chair.

7. We _____ (not) get cheap tickets, so we're not going to Europe

   this summer.

8. Jay _____ do back flips off the diving board when he was

   12 years old, but he (not) _____ now.

9. Andrea _____ get another ticket for the fashion show next week,

   so we _____ all go together.

10. Last week, I _____ buy a bunch of books on sale!

2 Practice

Answer the questions with your own ideas. Write complete sentences in the tenses given.

1. Can you write html code?

   _____.

2. Are you able to wiggle your ears?

   _____.

3. Could you whistle using your fingers when you were a child?

   _____.

4. Are you able to touch your nose with your tongue?

   _____.

5. Could you do magic tricks when you were younger?

   _____.

6. Can't you flip your eyelids inside out?

   _____.

7. Weren't you able to curl your tongue?

   _____.

8. Will you be able to walk on your hands if you practice?

   _____.

9. Won't you be able to change a flat tire if I show you how?

   _____.

10. Couldn't you run fast as a child?

    _____.

3 Practice

Answer the questions using *can* or *be able to* and your own ideas.

1. The cat's up our tree. How can we get him down?

   You can wait for him to get down by himself. You can call

   the fire department. You can climb up after him.

2. How can you get in your apartment when you lock your keys inside?

_____.

3. How will you be able to start your car if the battery is dead?

_____.

4. How can you call someone if you don't have their number?

_____.

5. How can you travel globally with very little money?

_____.

6. How can you decorate your apartment without spending a lot of money?

_____.

* **Bonus:** In one room there are three light switches. In another room there are three lights. How can you determine which switch turns on which light by going into each room only one time?
  Note: There are no holes in the walls, special tools, mirrors, equipment, or other people to help you.

4 | Practice

Read the paragraph on the Mayans and their accomplishments. Write sentences about them with *could* or *were able to*. More than one answer may be possible.

The Mayans, a group of ancient people that lived in modern day Mexico, Belize, Guatemala, and Honduras, existed from about 2000 B.C. to A.D. 1500. At the peak of their civilization, they were builders, artists, astronomers, farmers, and mathematicians. They predicted eclipses, studied the planets and constellations, and understood the lunar cycle. They built cities, observatories, palaces, ball fields, reservoirs for water storage, and temples, all without metal tools! They cleared the jungle to make farmland and grew cotton, corn, beans, and other vegetables. They developed three calendar systems, including one that has a 360-day year, and used a writing system which combined pictographs and sound characters.

1. _The Mayans could/were able to tell time_____.

2. _____.

3. _____.

4. _____.

5. _____ .

6. _____ .

7. _____ .

6c Must, Have To, and Have Got To to Express Obligation and Necessity

Student Book p. 154

5 Practice

Read the rules about driving. Match the verbs on the left with the ideas on the right. Then write sentences using *have to* or *must*.

__e__ **1.** stop completely   **a.** when you back up

_____ **2.** change oil   **b.** to change gears

_____ **3.** step on clutch   **c.** at all times

_____ **4.** turn headlights on   **d.** every 2,500 miles

_____ **5.** get insurance   **e.** at red lights

_____ **6.** signal   **f.** when driving at night

_____ **7.** wear seatbelts   **g.** when you buy a car

_____ **8.** look behind you   **h.** before you turn

1. *You must stop completely at red lights* _____ .

2. _____ .

3. _____ .

4. _____ .

5. _____ .

6. _____ .

7. _____ .

8. _____ .

Bonus Answer: Turn on one switch and let it stay on for an hour or so. Turn it off and flip a different switch. Go into the room with the lights. Find the light that's hot—that one is connected to the first switch. The light that's on goes to the second switch, and the cool light that is off goes with the third switch.

Practice

**Kate and Pedro are talking about rules in the woodworking class. Complete the
sentences with *must, have got to,* or the correct tense of *have to*. More than one
answer may be possible.**

Kate: Last year, we _____ wear our safety glasses all the time.
                                  1

Pedro: That's Mr. Thompson's strictest rule this year, too. We _____
                                                                            2

        wear them all the time.

Kate: What's the rule about equipment? When I took the class, we

        _____ return equipment at the end of each week.
                    3

Pedro: We _____ return equipment after two days, but next year,
                    4

        we _____ return equipment the same day it's checked out.
                    5

Kate: Yeah, I've heard the accident rule is changing next year, too. Last year, we

        _____ report all accidents within a week. Next year, we
                    6

        _____ report them immediately.
                    7

Pedro: At least some rules are staying the same! This year in class, each person

        _____ keep their work area clean, and next year each
                    8

        person _____ keep their work area clean, too.
                        9

Kate: That makes sense. I _____ keep my area clean when I took the class.
                                  10

Pedro: It's all just common sense. We just _____ follow
                                                        11

        Mr. Thompson's instructions. He is very clear about that! And students next year

        _____ follow even stricter rules—or else!
                    12

7 Practice

**Read the article about guinea pigs. Then write how to take care of them using *have
to, have got to,* or *must.***

Guinea Pigs Make Wonderful Pets!

If you love animals, but have a small apartment,
why not get a guinea pig (or two)! Guinea pigs can
make wonderful pets. Guinea pigs like company, so think
about getting a couple (two females or two males, unless
you want lots of baby guinea pigs).

Guinea pigs are affectionate and easy to take care of. They need vitamin C, vegetables, and clean water every day. Guinea pigs like clean cages, so be sure to clean them every three or four days. Newspaper is fine for the bottom of the cage. Guinea pigs are very gentle creatures; so don't make sudden movements or very loud noises near them. They need a safe place to hide and sleep in their cage. Guinea pigs can live ten years, so if you want one, be sure you can make the commitment to take care of him or her for that long.

1. *You have to be ready to take care of one for about ten years before you get one* .

2. _____ .

3. _____ .

4. _____ .

5. _____ .

6. _____ .

8 Practice

Read the rapid-speech sentences. Write the full forms.

1. "Billy's gotta stop missing so many classes."

   Billy has got to stop missing so many classes .

2. "Sorry, I gotta get going."

   _____ .

3. "What did we hafta do?"

   _____ .

4. "We hatta empty the trash."

   _____ .

5. "Deborah hasta get up at 3:00 A.M. every morning."

   _____ .

6. "Yuichiro and Emiko'll hafta study before they'll be able to do anything else!"

   _____ .

Write sentences using the correct tense of *have to* or *have got to*. Use the hints and your own ideas.

1. What did you have to do today to get ready for school?

   brush teeth   get up

   get dressed   shower

   a. *I had to get up at 6:00*   .

   b. _____ .

   c. _____ .

   d. _____ .

2. What will your friends have to do before they will be able to go on vacation?

   arrange for a petsitter   make hotel reservations

   book their flights   take their exams

   a. _____ .

   b. _____ .

   c. _____ .

   d. _____ .

3. What did people have to do 200 years ago?

   candles   grow food   horses

   a. _____ .

   b. _____ .

   c. _____ .

4. It's the beginning of the school year. What does Lucy have to do to get ready?

   buy textbooks   rent an apartment

   find a part-time job   set up her computer

   a. _____ .

   b. _____ .

   c. _____ .

   d. _____ .

6d *Not Have To* and *Must Not* to Express Prohibition and Lack of Necessity

Student Book p. 157

10 Practice

Mrs. Devine is taking her son to the opera for the first time. Match her instructions on the left with the ideas on the right.

_____ **1.** We don't have to drive.

_____ **2.** You don't have to wear a tuxedo.

_____ **3.** You mustn't lose the tickets.

_____ **4.** We mustn't be late

_____ **5.** You mustn't have your cell phone turned on.

_____ **6.** You don't have to play a musical instrument

a. A suit is fine.

b. to enjoy the performance.

c. It's standard policy.

d. We're taking a limo.

e. because we won't be allowed in.

f. They're irreplaceable.

11 Practice

A father is giving his daughters a lecture about life. Complete the sentences with *have to, not have to,* or *mustn't.*

You _____ always try to tell
                    1

the truth. You may not be able to do it all the time,

but you _____ try. You
                   2

_____ gossip about others because
        3

that hurts them. You _____ try to
                         4

control other people either. You _____
                                      5

take good care of yourself. You _____
                                      6

treat other people the way you want to be treated.

You _____ take on too many
          7

projects. You _____ do for others what they can do for themselves.
                  8

You _____ forgive other people because it only hurts you if you don't.
         9

You _____ try to make the world a better place.
        10

What are some rules that you live by? Use *have to* or *mustn't* in your answers.

1. _____.

2. _____.

3. _____.

|12| Practice

Read the paragraph on photography. Complete the sentences with *have to* or *not have to* in the correct verb tense.

When photography was invented,

photographers _____
                          1
hold the exposure for several minutes to

get a clear image. Now, of course, people

_____ use film cameras
            2
because digital cameras are very convenient.

When you used a film camera, you

_____ keep the back of the camera closed until you developed the
           3
film. When you bought film, you _____ get the right speed and
                                              4
exposure for the light and conditions. Now, if you don't have a camera, you

_____ pay hundreds of dollars for one because there are so many
           5
disposable ones on the market. In the future, people _____ use film
                                                                    6
at all. Photographers _____ carry so much special equipment. In the
                                 7
past, they _____ spend a lot of time developing film in the darkroom.
                     8
In the future, photographers _____ do that either.
                                          9

13 Practice

Complete the sentences with your own ideas.

1. Customer service representatives have to _try and help you_, but they don't
   have to _fix the computer_.

2. Hairstylists have to _____,
   but they don't have to _____.

3. A musician has to _____,
   but he or she doesn't have to _____.

4. Housekeepers have to _____,
   but they don't have to _____.

5. Good friends have to _____,
   but they don't have to _____.

6. A gardener has to _____,
   but she or he doesn't have to _____.

7. Children have to _____,
   but they don't have to _____.

8. A couple has to _____,
   but they don't have to _____.

14 Practice

Read the statements. Circle *Agree* or *Disagree* and explain your answer.

1. You don't have to have a college degree to get a good job.

   (Agree)   Disagree   _If you are passionate about something,_
                            you can get a good job without a degree.

2. Teachers mustn't hit students.

   Agree   Disagree   _____

3. Students mustn't sleep in class.

   Agree   Disagree   _____

4. You don't have to have a lot of money to be happy.

   Agree   Disagree   _____

5. Children mustn't talk to strangers.

   Agree   Disagree   _____

6. You mustn't make sudden moves around wild animals.

   Agree   Disagree   _____

7. People mustn't eat meat.

   Agree   Disagree   _____

8. People don't have to get married to have children.

   Agree   Disagree   _____

9. You don't have to wrap gifts before you give them.

   Agree   Disagree   _____

10. A society doesn't have to have rules.

   Agree   Disagree   _____

6e *Should, Ought To,* and *Had Better* to Give Advice

Student Book p. 159

15 Practice

Read the sentences with *had better* and write the possible consequences. Use *or* in your answers.

1. The class had better leave now, <u> or they'll miss the bus</u>.

2. The children had better not eat so much ice cream, _____.

3. You'd better be careful working so close to the grill, _____.

4. My wife and I'd better stop spending so much money, _____.

5. Jin had better start paying more attention in class, _____.

6. I think we'd better call a technician, _____.

7. The gardener had better water the yard today, _____.

8. I'd better get a job soon, _____.

9. I'd better work out more, _____.

10. I had better _____.

16 Practice

Read the following problems. Write suggestions using *should*, *shouldn't*, or *ought to*.

1. stolen laptop <u>You should call the police and file a report.</u> (OR)
<u>You should ask if anyone saw anything.</u>

2. depression

_____.

_____.

3. marital problems

_____.

_____.

4. a bad haircut

_____.

_____.

5. forgetfulness

_____.

_____.

6. high gasoline prices

_____.

_____.

7. insomnia

_____.

_____.

8. dyslexia

_____.

_____.

9. anorexia

_____.

_____.

10. a haunted house

_____.

_____.

17 Practice

Read the dialogues. Think of an appropriate situation for the responses.

1. Ryan: <u>*Ellen just yelled at me in front of everyone at my desk.*</u>

   Hideki: That's terrible!

   Rob: You should talk to her supervisor.

2. Jerome: _____.

   Chandra: That's great!

   Peggy: We should celebrate! Let's call everyone.

3. David: _____.

   Elsie: Well, I understand, but I think you should apologize to her.

4. Beth: _____.

   Ed: Really? You should call the police.

5. Michael: _____.

   Deborah: That's too bad.

   Kevin: You should come to the study sessions. They really help me.

6. Marissa: _____.

   Kyle: That looks terrible! You should put a bandage on that.

7. Gerald: _____.

   Krystal: You did? You should ask for a raise.

18 Practice

Read the questions and give advice using *should (not), ought to,* or *had better*.

1. What should someone do to learn another language?

   _____.

2. What should someone do if he or she is in a car accident?

   _____.

3. What should someone do if their computer crashes?

   _____.

4. What should people do if they have a lot of work to do, but they're too tired to do it?

_____.

5. What should someone do to live a better, healthier life?

_____.

6f   *Should Have* and *Ought To Have* to Express Regret or a Mistake

Student Book p. 161

19   **Practice**

Read the statements with *should have* and *shouldn't have*. Then write the reality or mistake of each situation.

1. They should have told you when they were going to come back.

They didnt tell you when they were coming back, and now

you feel it was a mistake   .

2. I shouldn't have eaten so many cherries. I don't feel very good right now.

_____.

3. We should have spent more time on our presentation.

_____.

4. My brother should have returned the library book two days ago.

_____.

5. You should have introduced yourself to our new neighbors.

_____.

6. Ugh. I just got off the phone with Angie. I should have let the machine pick it up.

_____.

7. The homeowners said they shouldn't have left the paint cans so close to the furnace.

_____.

8. You argue so much that you should have been a lawyer!

_____.

Practice

Kija Lee is a reporter. She's asking people on the street about regrets they have.
Read their statements and write their regrets.

A. Kija: Excuse me, sir. Could I ask you a question?

Andy: Sure.

Kija: Do you have any regrets?

Andy: Well, I should have gone to college when I had the chance. But I think it's too late now.

Regret: _Andy didn't go to college_   .

And last year I gave my wife a vacuum cleaner for her birthday. I shouldn't have done that!

Regret: _____.

B. Kija: Ma'am. How about you? Do you have any regrets?

Ms. Kim: Well, I should have accepted that job in Vietnam. It was a great opportunity.

Regret: _____.

And I shouldn't have started smoking again. It's so hard to quit!

Regret: _____.

C. Kija: Excuse me, sir. I'm talking with people about regrets. Do you have any that you'd like to share with our readers?

Pierre: I should have checked my parking meter earlier. Look! I got a ticket.

Regret: _____.

No, but seriously. I should have taken my family to the beach for our last vacation. We rented a cabin in the mountains, and it rained every day, and we were without power for most of the time. It was not fun.

Regret: _____.

D. Kija: Excuse me. Do you have any regrets?

You: I should have _____.

Regret: _____.

And I shouldn't have _____.

Regret: _____.

21 Practice

Read the rapid-speech sentences. Write the full forms.

1. "You shoulda been there. It was a riot!"

You should have been there. _____

2. "We better get going."

_____.

3. "Tommy oughta've moved to France."

_____.

4. "We coulda lent you the money."

_____.

5. "Kirk musta gotten lost. Otherwise, he woulda been here by now."

_____.

6. "Do we hafta do this right now?"

_____.

7. "Who shoulda done this?"

_____.

8. "Spock always hasta solve the problems on the ship."

_____.

Practice

Read the situations and complete the sentences. Use the words in parentheses and your own ideas. Be sure to use *not* if you write a negative sentence.

1. Yesterday the electric company was working on the utility pole outside my house. This morning when I looked outside, the pole was on fire! Luckily, the fire department came quickly and put out the fire.

   a. The crew (must) *must have done something wrong yesterday* .

   (OR) *They must not have fixed it* .

   b. The fire (could) *could have spread to other houses* .

   c. The crew (should) *should have made sure their work was*

   finished yesterday .

2. A young couple moved into the apartment next to me last month. Today I saw the woman packing boxes and carrying suitcases to her car. I haven't seen the man in a while.

   a. They (may) _____ .

   b. She (must) _____ .

   c. They (should) _____ .

3. At Maureen's favorite seafood restaurant yesterday, she tried crab for the first time. She usually has shrimp, but she wanted to try something different. An hour after lunch, Maureen got sick.

   a. She (must) _____ .

   b. She (could) _____ .

   c. She (should) _____ .

4. Zoe is a software consultant. She bills her customers every month. Last month she changed her accounting software, and she hasn't received any checks yet this month.

   a. She (must) _____ .

   b. She (should) _____ .

   c. She (could) _____ .

Practice

Answer the questions. Write sentences with *should have* or *shouldn't have*.

1. In your opinion, what is a mistake or decision that your government has made that you disagree with. What should (not) they have done?

   _____

   _____.

2. What is a mistake or decision that your best friend has made that you disagree with? What should (not) he or she have done?

   _____

   _____.

3. What is a mistake or decision that your parents have made that you disagree with? What should (not) they have done?

   _____

   _____.

6g *Be Supposed To* to Express Expectation

Student Book p. 164

24 **Practice**

Rachel and Yuri are teaching their children table manners. Write sentences with *be supposed to* or *not be supposed to* and the following ideas.

1. put elbows on the table

   You're not supposed to put your elbows on the table .

2. wait until everyone is seated before starting to eat

   _____.

3. chew with your mouth open

   _____.

4. say you don't like something

   _____.

   leave it on your plate

   _____.

5. put your napkin in your lap

_____.

6. cover your mouth and say "excuse me" if you burp

_____.

7. reach across the table to get something you want

_____.

ask someone politely to pass it to you

_____.

What are some other manners that children are taught?

1. _____.

2. _____.

3. _____.

25 Practice

Read the sentences about Holly and Steve meeting friends at a concert. Write possible ideas for why their plans went wrong. Answer the questions.

1. We were supposed to meet Betty and Mike at 7:00, _but we never met them_.

2. We were supposed to leave our house at 6:00, but _____

_____.

3. They were supposed to call one of us on our cell phones if we missed each other,

but _____.

4. We were supposed to have dinner with them, but _____.

5. There were supposed to be fireworks after the concert, but _____

_____.

6. It wasn't supposed to rain, but _____.

Read the statements. Fill in _T_ if the statement is true and _F_ if the statement is false.

1. Holly and Steve met Betty and Mike at the concert. (T) (F)

2. Holly and Steve didn't leave their house at 6:00. (T) (F)

3. They all ate dinner together. (T) (F)

4. There were fireworks. (T) (F)

5. It didn't rain. (T) (F)

SELF-TEST

A **Choose the best answer, A, B, C, or D, to complete the sentence. Mark your answer by darkening the oval with the same letter.**

1. The Browns _____ go camping with us.

   A. might could   Ⓐ Ⓑ Ⓒ Ⓓ
   B. may be able to
   C. can to
   D. didn't could

2. Jake _____ move the sofa. He found his keys on the bed.

   A. didn't must to   Ⓐ Ⓑ Ⓒ Ⓓ
   B. must to
   C. have to
   D. didn't have to

3. The firm _____ better sign the contract tomorrow, or they'll miss the opportunity.

   A. had   Ⓐ Ⓑ Ⓒ Ⓓ
   B. have
   C. ought to
   D. should

4. The new law says that drivers _____ block the sidewalk.

   A. must not   Ⓐ Ⓑ Ⓒ Ⓓ
   B. don't must
   C. should to
   D. ought to

5. Theresa _____ returned the phone call, but she didn't get the message until this morning.

   A. had to   Ⓐ Ⓑ Ⓒ Ⓓ
   B. should
   C. should have
   D. was able to

6. The women _____ to meet their trainer at 6:30 A.M.

   A. must   Ⓐ Ⓑ Ⓒ Ⓓ
   B. are supposed
   C. should
   D. had better

7. You _____ told her your opinion. She didn't ask you for it.

   A. didn't have to   Ⓐ Ⓑ Ⓒ Ⓓ
   B. should
   C. could
   D. shouldn't have

8. I think we _____ better compare prices before we decide which DVD player to get.

   A. should   Ⓐ Ⓑ Ⓒ Ⓓ
   B. could
   C. had
   D. must

9. Miriam _____ turn down the oven, but she turned it up instead. Now the pie is burned.

   A. is supposed to   Ⓐ Ⓑ Ⓒ Ⓓ
   B. was able to
   C. was supposed to
   D. had better to

10. Helen _____ email me back, but she did.

   A. mustn't   Ⓐ Ⓑ Ⓒ Ⓓ
   B. didn't have to
   C. had to
   D. supposed to

B **Find the underlined word or phrase, A, B, C, or D, that is incorrect. Mark your answer by darkening the oval with the same letter.**

1. Frankie <u>has</u> finish the paper tonight
   A
   because he <u>won't be</u> <u>able</u> <u>to</u> tomorrow.
   B **C** **D**

   Ⓐ Ⓑ Ⓒ Ⓓ

2. Karl <u>should</u> <u>have</u> <u>read</u> the directions
   A **B** **C**
   before he started playing the game. He
   <u>better</u> take a look at them now.
   D

   Ⓐ Ⓑ Ⓒ Ⓓ

3. Jay <u>shouldn't have</u> accepted the position.
   A
   He <u>can't</u> the job. He's <u>supposed</u> <u>to</u> tell
   B **C** **D**
   them tomorrow that he quits.

   Ⓐ Ⓑ Ⓒ Ⓓ

4. I'll <u>have to</u> <u>check</u> my calendar, but we
   A **B**
   <u>may</u> able <u>to go</u> with you.
   C **D**

   Ⓐ Ⓑ Ⓒ Ⓓ

5. Someone <u>is</u> supposed <u>come</u> tomorrow to
   A **B**
   look for the leak. I <u>couldn't</u> climb up
   C
   there, so I <u>can't</u> fix it.
   D

   Ⓐ Ⓑ Ⓒ Ⓓ

6. You <u>should</u> called the architect before we
   A
   left. She <u>was</u> <u>supposed to</u> have the plans
   B **C**
   ready but she doesn't. Now what are we
   <u>supposed to</u> do?
   D

   Ⓐ Ⓑ Ⓒ Ⓓ

7. Sue and I <u>ought to</u> <u>have</u> <u>went</u> to the gym,
   A **B** **C**
   but we <u>couldn't</u> wake up this morning.
   D

   Ⓐ Ⓑ Ⓒ Ⓓ

8. High school students <u>must</u> wear uniforms.
   A
   Girls <u>mustn't</u> <u>wear</u> short skirts, and boys
   B **C**
   <u>don't must</u> wear jeans.
   D

   Ⓐ Ⓑ Ⓒ Ⓓ

9. You're <u>supposed</u> to offer your seat to the
   A
   elderly. You <u>don't had to</u>, but <u>you</u> <u>should</u>.
   B **C** **D**

   Ⓐ Ⓑ Ⓒ Ⓓ

10. I <u>can drive</u> here because I have a driver's
    A
    license. Yesterday, I <u>could</u> rent a car. I
    B
    <u>was</u> <u>able to</u> get a good price on it, too.
    C **D**

    Ⓐ Ⓑ Ⓒ Ⓓ

UNIT 7 MODALS II

7a *Shall, Let's, How About, What About, Why Don't, Could, and Can to Make Suggestions*

Student Book p. 174

[1] Practice

Edna and Lucy are looking for somewhere to have lunch. Complete the sentences with *how about, what about, shall, could,* or *can*. More than one answer may be possible.

Edna: This place looks interesting.

_____ we have lunch here?
                  1

Lucy: Okay. _____ just
                      2

having a light lunch? Then we

_____ go for a run later.
             3

Edna: All right. That's a good idea.

They go into the restaurant.

Edna: _____ we sit by the window?
                    4

Lucy: Definitely. That's a nice view of the bay.

Edna (*to server*): Hello. _____ sitting near the window? Is that possible?
                                5

Server: Yes, of course.

Edna: Hmm. I don't know what to order.

Server: Well, _____ trying the special? It's chicken salad, and it has
                       6

chicken, raisins, and walnuts in it.

Edna: I'm allergic to walnuts. Maybe the chef _____ leave them out.
                                                          7

Server: I'm sorry. It's already made. _____ the penne with spring
                                              8

vegetables? It comes with salad and garlic bread.

Edna: That sounds perfect.

Lucy: I'd like the same thing, but I don't really like garlic bread.

Server: I _____ ask the chef to give you plain bread instead.
              9

Lucy: Thanks. I'd appreciate that.

Server: _____ something to drink?
                    10

Edna: I'll have iced tea, please.

Lucy: Just water for me, thanks.

2 │ Practice

**Read the dialogue between two college roommates. Complete the sentences with *let's,*
how about, what about, could, or *can.* More than one answer may be possible.**

Michele: We have two hours before class. What do you want to do?

Natalie: <u>How about/What about</u> going home and taking a nap?
                        1

Michele: I don't want to do that. _____ do some shopping. We
                                            2

          _____ check out that new shoe store on Pine.
                    3

Natalie: Or, we _____ go to the library and take a nap.
                            4

Michele: Natalie! I don't want to take a nap!

Natalie: Okay, okay. _____ getting some coffee then? I'm really sleepy.
                                5

Michele: Okay. There's a coffee shop next to the shoe store. _____ go
                                                                            6

          there first.

3 │ Practice

**The phrases of suggestion in the following sentences are incorrect. Rewrite the
sentences correctly three different ways using *how about, let's,* and *why don't.*
Add question marks if necessary.**

1.   <u>How about turn on</u> some music.

     <u>How about turning on some music?</u>   **(OR)**

     <u>Let's turn on some music.</u>   **(OR)**

     <u>Why don't we/you turn on some music?</u>

2.   <u>Why don't order</u> a pizza.

     _____

     _____

     _____

3. <u>Let's us meet</u> at my house.

_____

_____

_____

4. <u>Let's not taking</u> the highway.

_____

_____

_____

5. <u>Why don't taking</u> my car.

_____

_____

_____

6. <u>How about we going</u> now.

_____

_____

_____

7. <u>Why we don't take</u> some more time before we decide.

_____

_____

_____

8. <u>Let's we go</u> to the lake this weekend. It's going to be beautiful.

_____

_____

_____

9. <u>How about not play</u> card games for a change.

_____

_____

_____

10. <u>Let's going</u> out for dinner.

_____

_____

_____

4 Practice

A friend doesn't know what to do with his/her future. Write suggestions using _how about_, _what about_, _could_, and _why don't_.

You could take classes to find out what you're interested in.

Why don't you make an appointment with a career counselor?

_____

_____

7b _Prefer, Would Prefer,_ and _Would Rather_ to Express Preference
Student Book p. 176

5 Practice

Complete the sentences with _prefer_ or _would rather_ and _to_ or _than_ if necessary.

Laura: I'm thinking about planting vegetables in our garden. What do you think?

Kevin: Really? I _____ have a flower garden.
₁

Laura: But we live so far away from the

grocery store, I _____ grow my own
₂

tomatoes _____ go eight miles. I also _____ the
₃ ₄

flavor of fresh vegetables _____ store bought ones.
₅

Kevin: Yes, but a vegetable garden takes more time than a flower garden. When I get

home from work, I _____ relaxing _____
₆ ₇

watering and weeding the garden.

Laura: You won't have to do anything. I _____ take care of it myself anyway.
₈

106
Unit 7

6 Practice

Complete the sentences on the left with the endings on the right.

_____ 1. The children prefer water

_____ 2. Jessica would rather stay home

_____ 3. The royal family would prefer

_____ 4. Josh prefers cooking at home

_____ 5. Samantha would

a. than go to the movies.

b. to eating out.

c. rather eat tofu than seafood.

d. to juice.

e. not to comment on the situation.

7 Practice

Answer the questions with your own ideas. Explain your preferences.

1. Do you prefer to drive or take taxis?

   I prefer to take taxis. I don't like driving .

2. Would you rather spend money flying in first class or have the extra money to spend on your vacation?

   _____ .

3. Would you rather work for someone else or be your own boss?

   _____ .

4. Do you prefer spicy food to mild food?

   _____ .

5. When you go out, would you rather listen to a DJ or listen to a live band?

   _____ .

6. When you eat dinner, would you rather sit at a table or eat in front of the TV?

   _____ .

7. Do you prefer to work out at the gym or to go for a run outside?

   _____ .

8. Do you prefer eating at fast-food restaurants to eating at home?

   _____ .

8 Practice

Write as many questions and answers as you can using *would rather* and *prefer* and the following ideas.

1. history / physics

   - **Q:** _Would you rather study history or physics?_
     A: _I'd rather study physics than (study) history._
   - **Q:** _Do you prefer history to physics?_
     A: _No, I prefer physics (to history)._
   - **Q:** _Do you prefer studying history to studying physics?_
     A: _No, I prefer studying physics (to studying history)._
   - **Q:** _Do you prefer to study history?_
     A: _No, I don't._

2. work with numbers / work with people

   _____

   _____

   _____

   _____

3. drive a car / ride a motorcycle

   _____

   _____

   _____

   _____

4. gardening / reading

   _____

   _____

   _____

   _____

5. talk about your problems with other people / solve them by yourself

_____

_____

_____

_____

◆ 7c _May, Could,_ and _Can_ to Ask Permission

Student Book p. 180

9 **Practice**

Complete the sentences with _may, could,_ or _can._ More than one answer may be possible.

A. James: Excuse me. _____ I take a train schedule?
      ₁

   Clerk: Yes, you _____. Anything else?
      ₂

   James: Yes, _____ I also take the list of fares?
      ₃

   Clerk: No, I'm afraid you _____ because there isn't a complete list.
      ₄

   However, you _____ take anything on the counter.
      ₅

B. Danielle is talking to her best friend.

   Danielle: Claudia? It's me. _____ I talk to you for a minute?
      ₁

   Claudia: Yes, but I _____ talk for very long. What's up?
      ₂

   Danielle: I need a favor. _____ I use your bike tomorrow?
      ₃

   Claudia: Sure, you _____. Why?
      ₄

   Danielle: Mine has a flat tire, and I need to go by the post office.

   Claudia: No problem. You _____ borrow it anytime you need to.
      ₅

C. Sue: Sean, _____ my sister stay at your apartment for a few days
      ₁

   while you are out of town next week? She's in town interviewing.

   Sean: That's fine. She _____ stay there the whole week if she needs to.
      ₂

   Sue: _____ she give your number to people while she's there?
      ₃

   Sean: Yes, she _____, but she _____ give it to just anyone!
      ₄   ₅

D. Helga: _____ I smoke in here?
      ₁

   Host: Sorry, you _____. But you _____ smoke out on the patio.
      ₂   ₃

10 Practice

Write _a_ or _b_ beside each sentence to identify if the modal is used to talk about ability or permission.

_____ **1.** You may be excused.

_____ **2.** Could I look at your notes?

_____ **3.** Beverly could speak Italian fluently when she was in 6th grade.

_____ **4.** May I speak with you for a few minutes?

_____ **5.** You can have my sandwich. I'm not hungry.

_____ **6.** Cats can see in the dark.

_____ **7.** We can see our house from here!

_____ **8.** Could we sit near the front?

_____ **9.** Dad said we could go with you.

_____ **10.** Phil could easily run a 10K when he was younger.

a. ability

b. permission

11 Practice

Use the prompts to write dialogues with _may, could,_ or _can_. More than one modal may be correct.

1. You want to miss class. Ask your teacher. He gives you permission.

You: Mr. Faber, may I be absent tomorrow? My parents are coming for a visit .

Mr. Faber: Sure. That's no problem. Just ask someone about the homework .

2. You want to study in the United States. Ask your parents. They give you permission.

_____ ?

_____ .

3. Your boss wants you to work late. You have a dentist's appointment at 6:00.

_____ ?

_____ .

4. Your best friend wants to borrow your digital camera. The camera is broken.

_____ ?

_____ .

5. You want to see the dessert menu. Ask the server. He says "yes."

_____?

_____.

6. Your favorite movie star is sitting at a restaurant. Ask her for an autograph. She says "yes."

_____?

_____.

7. You want to try on a different pair of shoes. Ask the shoe salesperson. He says "yes."

_____?

_____.

7d *Will, Can, Could, Would,* and *Would You Mind* to Make Requests

Student Book p. 184

12 Practice

Read some common questions travelers ask in an English-speaking country. Complete the sentences with *could, would,* or *would you mind*.

1. _____ you tell me how to get to Sutter Street, please?

2. _____ you repeat that? I didn't hear what you said.

3. _____ repeating that?

4. _____ you tell me where the hotel is?

5. _____ you tell me if you have a vacancy, please?

6. _____ telling me where the nearest restaurant is?

7. _____ taking our photo, please?

8. _____ you take our photo, please?

9. _____ hailing a cab for me, please?

13

Practice

Jack is asking his friends to help him move. What do their responses mean? Write *accept* **or** *decline* **next to each answer.**

Jack: Hey, guys. Would you guys mind helping me move on Saturday?

1. _____*decline*_____ Walter: No way!

2. _____ Bob: Sure.

3. _____ Sanjay: Sorry.

4. _____ Kenneth: Yeah, okay.

5. _____ Sung Hee: I can't.

6. _____ Erik: No, I'd be happy to.

7. _____ Jerry: Yes, I'll be out of town.

How many people are going to help him move? _____

14

Practice

There are mistakes in the following sentences. Cross out incorrect words and add other words as necessary to correct them.

1. Would you mind ~~turn~~ *turning* down the music?

2. Would you going shopping with me?

3. **A:** Could you work late tonight?

   B: Yes, I could.

4. **A:** Would you picking up some butter?

   B: Sure.

5. Would you mind come with me?

6. **A:** Could you lend me your MP3 player?

   B: No, I couldn't. Sorry.

7. **A:** Would you mind not park there?

   B: Oh, sorry!

8. **A:** Would you helping me with this exercise?

   B: No problem.

15 Practice

Write requests based on the following information.

1. A friend of yours plays guitar. You would like to learn. Ask him/her.

    Could you teach me how to play guitar?

2. You need a ride to work because your car isn't working. Ask a coworker.

    _____

3. You still don't understand the unit. Ask your teacher to postpone the test.

    _____

4. The phone's ringing. You have just gotten out of the shower. Ask your roommate to answer it.

    _____

5. You and your roommate share housework, but he/she hasn't washed his/her dishes in a week. Ask them to.

    _____

6. Your girlfriend/boyfriend always talks during movies. Ask him/her to be quiet.

    _____

7. You need a new pair of glasses. The designer frames you really like cost $500. Ask a friend to loan you some money.

    _____

8. You're going to a party and your roommate has a new sweater that would look GREAT on you. Ask him/her to borrow it.

    _____

9. You are at a café and you need to use the restroom. Ask the clerk for the key.

    _____

7e *May, Might,* and *Could* to Express Possibility

Student Book p. 187

16 **Practice**

Write *a* or *b* beside each sentence to identify if the modal is used to talk about something that is/was possible or something that is/was impossible.

_____ 1. I couldn't have gone with you. I had to work.

_____ 2. You drove? Jin could have gone with you.

_____ 3. We may need to get gas soon.

_____ 4. He may have called, and we didn't hear the phone.

_____ 5. Joon Hee might take some online classes this summer.

_____ 6. The Leiers could have seen Notre Dame but they went to Versailles instead.

_____ 7. I couldn't have done it without your help.

_____ 8. Dr. O'Malley couldn't have driven this morning. His car's still in the driveway.

_____ 9. The sales team may finish their work by midnight if everything goes okay.

_____ 10. Sarah thinks she might get an "A" on her next test.

a. possible

b. impossible

17 **Practice**

Read the conversations. Answer the questions with *may, might,* or *could* to express possibility in the present.

1. Ana: What has happened to your computer?

Luke: I'm not sure. *It might have a virus.* (OR) *The server could be busy.*

Ana: What are you going to do if it doesn't work?

Luke: _____.

Ana: How are you going to finish the report?

Luke: I don't know. _____.

2. A: Wow. This is a really good salad. What's in it? What do you think?

B: I don't know. _____ or

_____.

3: A: How are you going to decorate your new home?

B: I'm not sure, yet. _____ in the living room,

but _____ in the bedrooms.

And _____ in the kitchen.

A: How about the back yard?

B: That's a problem. It's so big. _____.

4. A: How does that magician float in air?!

B: I don't really know, but _____.

5. A: I dreamt I was walking through a green room, and when I looked out the window,

I saw my best friend sitting in a tree waving at me. What do you think it means?

B: I have no idea, but _____ or

_____.

18 Practice

Answer the questions in two ways. Use *may, might,* or *could* + *have* + a past participle to express possibility in the past.

1. A: Why didn't Paige call you back last night?

B: _She might not have had time_ . (OR) _She could have been_
too busy last night .

2. A: Why didn't our English teacher assign any homework yesterday?

B: _____.

_____.

3. A: What has happened to Michael? He looks terrible.

B: I don't know. _____.

_____.

4. A: Do you know why Pedro quit his job last week?

B: _____.

_____.

5. A: Why did Karina start smoking again last summer?

 B: _____ .

_____ .

6. A: Why didn't Nikki introduce herself to you at the party?

 B: _____ .

_____ .

7. A: Whoa! Did you see that? I wonder why that car ran the red light!

 B: _____ .

_____ .

8. A: Have you seen Cheryl? Why has she cut her hair so short?

 B: _____ .

_____ .

---

19 Practice

Read the questions. Answer them with your own ideas. Use *may, might,* or *could + have* + a past participle to express possibility in the past.

1. How was Stonehenge built? Who built it?

 It could have been built by druids or ancient priests.

 It might have been built by aliens (just kidding!).

2. How did the dinosaurs become extinct?

 _____

 _____

3. How was the universe created?

 _____

 _____

Think of some other mysteries. Write possible explanations for them.

4. _____

 _____

5. _____

_____

6. _____

_____

7f *Should* and *Ought To* to Express Probability

Student Book p. 192

20 Practice

Complete the sentences with the verbs in parentheses. Use *should/ought to* + base verb for things that are probable in the present or future. Use *should/ought to* + *have* + past participle for things that were probable in the past.

1. They're working hard. They (feel) <u>*ought to feel/should feel*</u> exhausted at the end of their shift.

2. We just ate an hour ago! You (not, be) _____ hungry yet.

3. I gave the baby some medicine. She (stop) _____ coughing by now.

4. Roberto is really tired. He (sleep) _____ well tonight.

5. Lourdes bought the shoes last week. She (try) _____ them on already.

6. There was no traffic this morning. You (not, be) _____ late to the meeting.

7. We're going to a four-star restaurant. The food (taste) _____ superb, and the atmosphere (encourage) _____ diners to relax.

8. Your car used to be in good condition. You (sell) _____ it last year.

9. Mr. Potter (return) _____ soon. He just went to get a cup of coffee.

10. George (not, fail) _____ the exam. He'd studied most of the weekend!

21

Practice

**Complete the sentences about things that have probably happened using the
perfect modal form of *should* or *ought to* (*should* or *ought to* + *have*) and the verbs in
parentheses.**

1. The wedding is in 30 minutes. The flowers (arrive) __*should have arrived/*__

   __*ought to have arrived*__ by now.

2. Ann left the job over a month ago. They (post) _____

   the position.

3. Sam: Your cousin's knee was injured the last time I saw her.

   Bob: Yes, she (have) _____ knee surgery, but I haven't

   heard anything.

4. I mailed the package two weeks ago. You (receive) _____

   it by this week.

5. Let's go to the mall. It's late. The crowd (die down) _____.

6. Lucy and Bill are leaving on the 12th. They (get) _____

   their tickets by now.

7. Have you heard anything from the police? They (finish) _____

   the investigation.

8. Barbara is going on a diving trip next week. She (take) _____

   scuba diving lessons by now.

22 **Practice**

Read the sentences and use your own ideas to tell why the speaker uses *should* **or** *ought to* **+ a base verb or** *should/ought to* **+** *have* **+ a past participle.**

1. The opera is in 10 minutes. The audience ought to be seated by now.

   Normally at an opera, the audience arrives and is seated about

   15 minutes before the opera begins. We expect this.

2. The students started the test 90 minutes ago. They should have finished by now.

   _____

   _____.

3. The trip from downtown only takes 40 minutes. They ought to be back any time now.

   _____

   _____.

4. It's 9:30. The mail shouldn't arrive until noon.

   _____

   _____.

5. Let's call Jim. He shouldn't have left yet. It's only 7:30.

   _____

   _____.

6. Today, we should hear if the agent has accepted our offer on the new house.

   _____

   _____.

7. After your massage, you should feel pretty good.

   _____

   _____.

8. We're starting with advanced digital modeling. You should have learned the basics last semester.

   _____

   _____.

7g *Must, Must Not,* and *Can't* to Make Deductions

Student Book p. 194

23 Practice

Write *a* or *b* beside each sentence to identify if *can* or *can't* is used to talk about permission or deduction.

_____	**1.** Can I use your computer?	**a.** permission
_____	**2.** No, you can't.	**b.** deduction

_____ **3.** She left five minutes ago. She can't have gone too far.

_____ **4.** My children can only watch five hours of television a week.

_____ **5.** This bill can't be right. The waiter forgot to add on our dessert.

_____ **6.** Everyone can go to the museum today. It's free on Thursdays.

_____ **7.** That clock can't be right. My watch says it's 1:20.

_____ **8.** This coat can't be yours. Yours is on the floor over there.

_____ **9.** Can I adopt a dog, please?

_____ **10.** We can't adopt a dog until we have more time to spend with him or her.

24 Practice

Complete the deductions with *must* or *must not* and the ideas in parentheses.

1. That man is calling for help! He (know how to swim) *must not know how*

   *to swim*_____.

2. Everyone in that family has their own car. They (have a lot of money) _____

   _____.

3. Cindy has two dogs, three cats, and a canary. She (love animals) _____

_____.

4. I'm waving at Sherry, but she's not waving back. She (see us) _____

_____.

5. Toni screamed when she saw the spider. She (be afraid of them) _____

_____.

6. Jennifer's always upbeat. She (worry too much about small issues) _____

_____.

7. Tom and Danny haven't said two words to each other. They (be angry at each other)

_____.

8. Franklin never suggests we go to science fiction films. He (enjoy science fiction)

_____.

Complete the sentences with your own ideas.

9. This kitchen has everything! The people living here _____

_____.

10. You've finished this exercise already? Modals _____

_____.

25 | Practice

Match the sentences on the left with the past deductions on the right.

_____ **1.** Carl is dancing. I can't believe it!

_____ **2.** Oh, no. The dog threw up on the living room carpet.

_____ **3.** There's an ambulance across the street at the neighbor's.

_____ **4.** Kevin got directions off the Internet, but he's not here yet.

_____ **5.** My alarm didn't go off, and there are no lights.

a. Something must have happened.

b. The power must have gone off.

c. She must have eaten something that upset her stomach.

d. He must have taken lessons.

e. He must not have followed them correctly.

26 Practice

Read about Armand in high school and now. Write one deduction about the present using *must* and one about the past using *must have* or *must not have*.

In high school

1. Armand weighed 210 pounds.

2. He didn't date anyone in particular.

3. He moved to Seattle after graduation.

4. His twin sister went to the same high school.

5. Armand wore glasses.

6. He was quiet and shy.

Now

1. Armand weighs 190 pounds.

2. He's wearing a wedding ring.

3. He's looking for a house in his hometown.

4. His twin sister is not at the reunion.

5. Armand doesn't wear glasses.

6. He is talking to everyone and smiling a lot.

1. _Armand must work out regularly_ .

   (OR) _Armand must have started working out_ .

2. _____ .

   (OR) _____ .

3. _____ .

   (OR) _____ .

4. _____ .

   (OR) _____ .

5. _____ .

   (OR) _____ .

6. _____ .

   (OR) _____ .

27 **Practice**

Read Lucinda's schedule for yesterday. Read the conversation and complete the sentences with *can't have* or *couldn't have* and the verbs in parentheses. More than one answer may be possible.

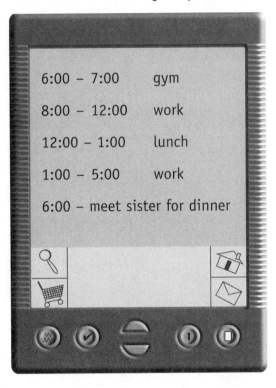

6:00 – 7:00	gym
8:00 – 12:00	work
12:00 – 1:00	lunch
1:00 – 5:00	work
6:00 –	meet sister for dinner

Paulo: Hey, Lucinda! I saw you at the deli yesterday around 11:30.

Lucinda: You (see) _can't have seen_ (OR) _couldn't have seen_ me, Paulo.
                                      1
             I was at work.

Paulo: Really? Well, I saw you again outside the bank at 1:30. I waved at you.

Lucinda: That (be) _____ me. I was at work then, too.
                                  2
             You (wave) _____ at me.
                                  3

Paulo: I did! And you smiled back.

Lucinda: I (smile) _____ at you. I wasn't there!
                                  4

Paulo: That's strange. You even said "hi."

Lucinda: I (say) _____ anything. Wait a minute.
                                  5
             Was 'I' wearing blue jeans?

Paulo: I think so.

Lucinda: Of course! You must have seen my twin sister, Linda.

7h The Progressive and Perfect Progressive Forms of Modals

Student Book p. 198

28 Practice

Read about Carole, Irene, and Ellen. Then write sentences about Irene and Ellen's schedule for this Tuesday using *should* or *could* in the progressive form.

Carole has two teenage daughters, Irene and Ellen.
Irene and Ellen help around the house.
These are Irene and Ellen's schedules for this Tuesday.

Ellen

Oct 11	S M **T** W T F S
8:00-3:15	study at school
3:45-5:15	do homework
5:15-5:45	straighten the living room
6:00-6:30	cook dinner
6:30	Mom comes home
7:15-7:30	wash (OR) dry & put away dishes
7:30-9:30	free time: watch TV, talk to friends, go online, visit friends

Irene

Oct 11	S M **T** W T F S
8:00-3:15	study at school
3:45-5:15	do homework
5:15-5:45	water the garden
6:00-6:30	cook dinner
6:30	Mom comes home
7:15-7:30	wash (OR) dry & put away dishes
7:30-9:30	free time: watch TV, talk to friends, go online, visit friends

1. It's 4:00, so Irene and Ellen

   should be doing their homework .

2. It's 5:30, so Irene _____ .

3. From 5:15 to 5:45, Ellen _____ .

4. At 6:00, Irene _____ ,

   or Ellen _____ .

5. Then, from 7:15 to 7:30, Irene _____ .

6. At the same time, Ellen _____ .

7. From 7:30 to 9:30, they _____, _____,

_____, or they _____.

29 Practice

It's Saturday. Carole is telling a friend about Irene and Ellen's responsibilities last Tuesday. Write sentences using *should* or *could* in the perfect progressive form.

1. Last Tuesday at 2:45, Irene and Ellen *should have been studying at school*.

2. At 3:45, they _____.

3. At 5:20, Ellen _____.

4. At the same time, Irene _____.

5. At 6:00, Irene _____,

   or Ellen _____.

6. At 7:15, Ellen _____.

7. At 8:00, they _____, _____,

   _____, or they _____.

30 Practice

You are sitting on a bench on the boardwalk at the beach. Complete the sentences with a modal *could, should, may, might,* or *must* in the progressive or perfect progressive form and the verbs in parentheses. More than one possibility is possible.

1. A woman is carrying a surfboard. She (walk) *could/may/might be walking*

   to the beach.

2. Her hair is wet, and she's wearing a wetsuit. She (surf) _____ earlier.

3. She seems tired. She (carry) _____ her surfboard for a while.

4. She stops. She (look) _____ for her jeep.

5. There are also two boys running past you. They (race) _____

   to the end of the boardwalk.

6. They are really out of breath! They (run) _____ all the way

   from the other end of the boardwalk.

7. The boys are slowing down. They (stop) _____.

8. They are laughing. They (have) _____ a great day at the beach!

31 Practice

Read the sentences about teenagers in a car accident. Write _C_ if the progressive or perfect progressive form is correct. Write _I_ if the progressive or perfect progressive form is incorrect.

_____ **1.** Those kids shouldn't have been standing so close to the highway.

_____ **2.** They could have been waited for a ride.

_____ **3.** Chao and Belinda must not have been hanging out with them.

_____ **4.** We should going to visit them in the hospital.

_____ **5.** They might be waiting for visitors.

_____ **6.** They must not have been paid attention to the cars.

_____ **7.** The police said the traffic light may not have been working correctly.

_____ **8.** They must have been talked loudly. They didn't hear the car coming.

_____ **9.** The doctor said they should be doing well in a couple of days or so.

32 Practice

Complete the sentences with your own ideas.

1. Instead of watching TV, I should be _helping my dad paint the basement_.

2. Instead of doing homework, I could be _____.

3. I should be _____

instead of writing email.

4. Tonight at 6:30, I might be _____.

5. Instead of going to school, I could be _____.

6. One year after I graduate, I might be _____.

7. Instead of spending money, I should be _____.

A Choose the best answer, A, B, C, or D, to complete the sentence. Mark your answer by darkening the oval with the same letter.

1. _____ we meet at the theater? We can go out to eat after the movie.

    A. Let's   Ⓐ Ⓑ Ⓒ Ⓓ
    B. Why don't
    C. How about it
    D. Let's not

2. We _____ stop by the ATM before we get to the restaurant.

    A. let's   Ⓐ Ⓑ Ⓒ Ⓓ
    B. why don't
    C. how about
    D. could

3. Bill prefers seeing movies on a big screen _____.

    A. than rent them   Ⓐ Ⓑ Ⓒ Ⓓ
    B. to rent them
    C. or rent them
    D. to renting them

4. Our management team _____ keep as many people as possible than let them go.

    A. prefers   Ⓐ Ⓑ Ⓒ Ⓓ
    B. would prefer
    C. would rather
    D. rather

5. **A:** Could we park here for just a minute?
   B: _____.

    A. Yes, you could   Ⓐ Ⓑ Ⓒ Ⓓ
    B. No, you couldn't
    C. No, you mayn't
    D. Yes, you can

6. _____ not smoking here? I'm allergic to cigarette smoke.

    A. Could you   Ⓐ Ⓑ Ⓒ Ⓓ
    B. Can you
    C. Would you mind
    D. Would you

7. Luckily, no one was home when the tree fell on the house. Someone _____ hurt.

    A. could have been   Ⓐ Ⓑ Ⓒ Ⓓ
    B. should have been
    C. may have been
    D. must have been

8. Toru _____ have paid for dinner. He left his wallet at home!

    A. shouldn't   Ⓐ Ⓑ Ⓒ Ⓓ
    B. can't
    C. may not
    D. could

9. _____ I borrow your car? I'll be very careful, I promise.

    A. Would   Ⓐ Ⓑ Ⓒ Ⓓ
    B. Will
    C. Shall
    D. Could

10. _____ he'll get the computer to work before we leave.

    A. Maybe   Ⓐ Ⓑ Ⓒ Ⓓ
    B. May be
    C. Might be
    D. Would be

Find the underlined word or phrase, A, B, C, or D, that is incorrect. Mark your answer by darkening the oval with the same letter.

1. Buddy <u>would rather</u> <u>stay</u> inside <u>than</u>
         A   B   C

<u>playing</u> outside with other children.
   D

Ⓐ Ⓑ Ⓒ Ⓓ

2. Suzie <u>would rather</u> <u>having</u> more time off
              A   B

<u>to</u> <u>working</u> a lot.
 C   D

Ⓐ Ⓑ Ⓒ Ⓓ

3. My grandson <u>maybe</u> sleeping, or he <u>could</u>
                       A   B

be playing music. He <u>should</u> be <u>thinking</u>
                          C   D

about his future!

Ⓐ Ⓑ Ⓒ Ⓓ

4. We <u>could</u> <u>go</u> to a spa, or <u>what about</u> <u>take</u>
         A   B   C   D

a bike trip through wine country?

Ⓐ Ⓑ Ⓒ Ⓓ

5. It's five? They <u>should be</u> <u>arrived</u> by now.
                      A   B

We <u>could have</u> <u>given</u> them a ride, but they
       C   D

wanted to walk.

Ⓐ Ⓑ Ⓒ Ⓓ

6. You <u>can</u> <u>have seen</u> me at the carnival
         A   B

yesterday! I was working at home.

<u>Maybe</u> you <u>saw</u> me the day before.
  C   D

Ⓐ Ⓑ Ⓒ Ⓓ

7. I don't know what's wrong. <u>Maybe</u> he
                                    A

fainted. He <u>could be</u> <u>had</u> a heart attack.
               B   C

The ambulance <u>should be arriving</u> soon.
                      D

Ⓐ Ⓑ Ⓒ Ⓓ

8. She <u>would prefer</u> <u>have</u> the gold one <u>to</u>
              A   B   C

<u>the silver one</u>.
      D

Ⓐ Ⓑ Ⓒ Ⓓ

9. You <u>should</u> <u>of</u> come! Everyone was there.
            A   B

I <u>could have</u> <u>picked</u> you up.
     C   D

Ⓐ Ⓑ Ⓒ Ⓓ

10. Jeanine must have <u>been</u> <u>sleeping</u> when I
                          A   B

called. She <u>prefers</u> <u>sleep</u> late on Saturdays.
               C   D

Ⓐ Ⓑ Ⓒ Ⓓ